Pay It Forward

A Map to Mentorship in Medicine

Andrea Sikora

DISCLAIMER

The information contained in this publication is advisory only and is not intended to replace sound clinical judgment or individualized patient care. The author disclaims all warranties, whether expressed or implied, including any warranty as the quality, accuracy, safety, or suitability of this information for any particular purpose.

ISBN: 978-1-946665-63-8

Cover Design: Ken Tackett

Developmental Editing: Kathleen Kendall-Tackett

Copyediting: Chris Tackett

Layout & Design: Nelly Murariu

This book is dedicated to
mentors and mentees.

A mind is a fire to be kindled,
not a vessel to be filled.
—Plutarch

CONTENTS

4: AN ONGOING JOURNEY 107

AUTHOR'S NOTE

Friends, we are traveling together. – **Rumi**

How do we care for those that have dedicated their lives to caring for others?

Most every facet of healthcare is defined by giving of yourself to someone else. No matter the particular domain within healthcare (the bedside, the classroom, the manager's office), healthcare professionals are asked to care for someone: patients, trainees, fellow employees.

Yet, much of healthcare education focuses on the nuts and bolts: how to interpret laboratory results, complete a physical exam, or fill a prescription. Though essential to being skillful clinicians, didactic training programs often overlook the myriad of other skills needed for a healthcare career. Helping the next generation navigate the inherent psychosocial challenges of career growth in healthcare is vital to retaining the best and brightest in the field and advancing the quality of the care that we provide.

Much of a healthcare professional's training is on the job. When I took my first faculty position, I was suddenly responsible for a dozen modules a year in the Doctor of Pharmacy curriculum yet had never taken a single class on teaching pedagogy. When asked to collaborate with a basic science laboratory, I had never run electrophoresis or used statistical software. I had no formal training in mental health or best practices in promotion of diversity, yet both were important when working with students. Neither my PharmD degree nor two years of residency required me to create a promotion dossier, learn how to network with other researchers across the globe, or develop an institutional protocol as part of a quality improvement initiative. Overwhelmed with new skills to master, and unsure if I was doing a good job, it was hard to calibrate my efforts and results. I felt lonely and inefficacious. It was mentorship that filled those gaps for me.

Put another way, while the foundation of healthcare may be based on textbook knowledge of pathophysiology and treatment, the ability to deliver care to patients, pursue new knowledge through scientific inquiry, and educate the next generation requires that healthcare providers develop high-level technical and psychosocial skills during a lifelong journey. You cannot learn to be a compassionate and skillful clinician, researcher, and educator in a classroom. This journey is best accompanied by caring mentors. Mentors are integral to this education process because they provide real-time insights into next steps for development and unique opportunities for experiences that supplement the classroom. Moreover, they create the supportive and nurturing environment necessary to both success and fulfillment. While mentorship is often discussed in corporate and other sectors, there is a unique difference in healthcare careers because loyalty is often focused to the profession and on the advancement of patient care (not the corporation). Yet, it is rarely part of the official curriculum.

Mentorship is the oft unspoken cornerstone to the development of a healthcare professional and their lifelong career of giving.

Mentorship focuses on authentic connection between individuals and is an antidote to many ills the healthcare system faces. It uniquely and irreplaceably enhances any training program or workplace. The numbers are compelling; people with mentors are more likely to be promoted, have salary raises, and achieve their career goals. Mentees are more productive and engaged, more satisfied with their careers, and more likely to stay at the organization. Moreover, it is rapidly implementable at the individual level. As such, mentorship is one of the most empowering gifts we can give or receive.

Mentorship is a lifelong journey invested in the growth and development of yourself and others. This book is intended to be a warm introduction to mentorship's power and an overview to the key concepts, attitudes, and skillsets that will be needed along the path of becoming both the best mentor and mentee one can be. It is an invitation to take part on an unforgettable journey and a map for getting started.

Ultimately, this book is a celebration of mentorship.

Stories reflect the author's recollections of past experiences. Names and certain details have been changed to protect both the mentors and mentees identities. Additionally, some events have been compressed, and dialogue has been recreated, but in the words of Tobias Wolff, *"I have done my best to make it tell a truthful story."*

Much have I learned from my teachers, even more have I learned from my colleagues, but from my students I have learned more than from anyone else. – **The Talmud**

A BRIEF HISTORY

Written over 2,000 years ago, the Hippocratic Oath is one of the oldest documents describing medical conduct. Although famous for the oft quoted "first, do no harm," it is notable that the Oath does not begin with this injunction but instead with lines discussing how the individual should view their teacher and the next generation. "I swear. . . to hold my teacher in this art equal to my own parents . . . to consider his family as my own brothers, and to teach them this art, if they want to learn it, without fee or indenture . . ."

This concept echoes a "pay it forward" approach in that a pupil honors the former teacher by that pupil passing along the craft, without regard to personal profit. The word "mentor" derives from a character in Homer's *Odyssey*. The goddess Athena assumed the appearance of a family friend, Mentor, to help guide the young Telemachus during a difficult journey. Interestingly, Mentor is an elderly man who does not always follow through and thus not a particularly effective "mentor" by today's standards. In fact, it is the goddess Athena who provides support and wisdom for Telemachus. One wonders if the more appropriate term for the concept of an experienced and trusted advisor providing insight and advice would be better termed an "Athena."

Various systems of mentorship throughout history include the guild-based economic system of the Middle Ages, the guru-disciple traditions practiced in Hinduism and Buddhism, and the discipleships practiced by Judaism and Christianity. A pattern of individuals of historical importance citing others with singular influence in their lives is also apparent (e.g., Martin Luther King with Dr. Benjamin Elijah Mays, Mozart with Haydn, Alexander the Great with Aristotle). Within medicine, William Osler and Harvey Cushing are a classic mentor-mentee duo, both becoming leaders in their fields. Residency can potentially be considered a modern-day permutation of this history, with assigned preceptors and advisors often functioning in mentoring roles. In such a way, residency formalizes the one-on-one nature of mentorship into a primary teaching modality. Modern mentorship is ever evolving.

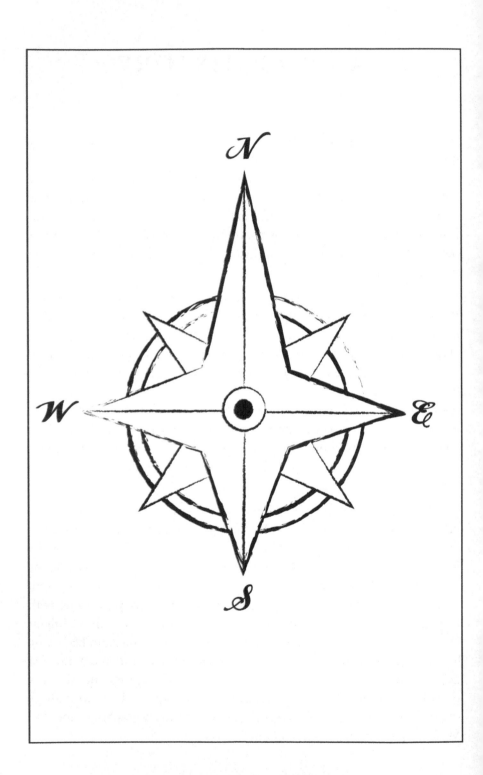

A MAP TO MENTORSHIP IN MEDICINE

This book is divided into four sections.

1. **Embarking:** The why, who, and what of mentorship
2. **Mentoring Mindsets:** The attitudes and beliefs of mentorship
3. **Logistics:** The practices of mentorship
4. **Ongoing Journey:** The sustainability of mentorship

1

EMBARKING

*This section introduces the
why, who, and what of mentorship.*

Men·tor·ship

/ˈmentôrSHip,ˈmentərSHip/

noun. A deliberate, effortful, and bi-directional relationship characterized by *mutual growth* and *shared altruism* with a primary goal of the personal and professional development of the mentee

Mutual Growth

A commitment to mutual growth is one of two hallmarks of an authentic, high-quality mentor-mentee relationship alongside shared altruism.

Growth refers to both personal and professional domains for individual development. The term captures the transformational process that includes reflection, planning, and action to improve individual thought processes, habits, knowledge, skills, and experiences that help an individual achieve their stated goals. Moreover, this growth is part of the ultimate self-actualization process, considered by Maslow as the highest order human need of fully realizing an individual's potential for personal fulfillment. Growth is recognized as intrinsic to healthcare worker motivation and is a marker of the modern-day workplace, wherein individuals seek meaning and personal development as high priorities in job selection.[1]

Mutual refers to the growth process being bi-directional and reciprocal in nature. Both the mentor and the mentee have a commitment to not only their individual growth but to the growth of the other. As such, each individual enters the relationship with the intent to give and to take. The ability to provide open feedback is inherent to such a relationship and viewing each other as stewards of development is important for modern-day mentorship.

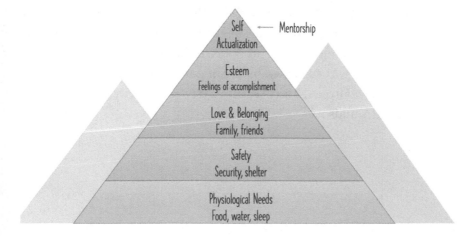

Shared Altruism

al·tru·ism /ˈaltrōoˌizəm/

noun. The belief in or practice of disinterested and selfless concern for the well-being of others

Shared altruism is the second core principle of a mentoring relationship. Achieving full growth is not feasible without this element of altruism, as giving is foundational to full self-actualization. Moreover, as Saint Francis of Assisi says, "It is by giving that we receive." Mentorship is an ultimate form of a give and take relationship, and it is a two-way street with both individuals getting out of the relationship what they invest into the relationship. Lao Tzu wrote, "If you would take, you must first give, this is the beginning of intelligence."

Mentors nurture and guard the growth and wellbeing of the mentee when asking questions, giving advice, and suggesting opportunities. Professionally, the actions of both individuals are reflections of the other. Both individuals share responsibility to think about how actions affect the other, reaching out first to check-in, and being deliberate about commitments to each other.

Viewing mentorship as a means of plugging into the deep interconnectedness of life is valuable. We are able to go further together, and this is a tradition seen throughout the natural world. Indeed, in *The Hidden of Life of Trees,* Peter Wohlleben writes, "But the most astonishing thing about trees is how social they are. The trees in a forest care for each other, sometimes even going so far as to nourish the stump of a felled tree for centuries after it was cut down by feeding it sugars and other nutrients, and so keeping it alive...This is because a tree can be only as strong as the forest that surrounds it."

A single act of kindness throws out roots in all directions, and the roots spring up and make new trees. – **Amelia Earhart**

Why Mentorship?

MYTH: Mentorship is a buzzword. It doesn't produce results.

Mentorship can feel like just another buzzword used in leadership seminars or a gimmick without substance, like when a fast food chain found that recognizing employees' efforts with certificates of achievement (instead of pay raises) led to cost-efficient decreases in employee turn-over.[2] Let's discuss how having a mentor affects the bottom line. In a famous study of Sun Microsystems, Gartner (a research and advisory firm) conducted an analysis of the financial impact of mentoring. The numbers were striking not only for their benefit to the corporation (higher retention rates are known to be cost-saving) but also for the individuals (who had more promotions and pay raises).[3]

- **Mentees were promoted 5x more frequently** than non-mentees
- **25% of mentees had salary increases** compared to 5% of non-mentees
- **Retention rates were 22% higher for mentees** and **20% higher for mentors** than those who did not participate in either role

McArthur Mentoring states that more than 70% of Fortune 500 companies have invested in mentorship programs because they have strong return on investment for performance and creativity. Moreover, recent generations (e.g., Millennials) are more likely to stay in positions with mentorship because it enhances meaning and personal development. In a large meta-analysis of mentorship, even after adjusting for co-variates like gender, race, core self-evaluations, tenure, education, and job performance, mentorship showed benefits in career satisfaction.[4]

In healthcare, the results are also notable: mentor-mentee programs increase publishing rates[5] and metrics of faculty career development,[3] reduce burnout,[6,7] support diversity, equity, and inclusion,[8] and increase career satisfaction.[9,10] A brief PubMed search shows mentorship benefits across most every discipline in medicine, nursing, pharmacy, and beyond. As healthcare faces higher rates of burn-out and attrition from the field, mentorship may be an important intervention to improve wellness of our healthcare team.

The Balance of Give and Take

*Every man must decide whether he will walk in
the light of creative altruism or in the darkness of
destructive selfishness.* – **Martin Luther King Jr**

Life is about relationships. Relationships support both personal fulfillment and career success. Most every healthcare career will include working in a team-based setting to deliver care. Though it may seem antithetical, the more generous an individual acts has a direct relationship to not only objective markers of success (e.g., positions, salary) but also psychosocial metrics of wellbeing (e.g., fulfillment, satisfaction). In Adam Grant's *Give and Take*[11], he notes that generosity leads to success. He explains that "givers" are characterized by this desire to be generous and to see other people benefit through their efforts as opposed to a "zero-sum" game where, in order for one person to win, another must lose. Givers can "get to the top without cutting others down, finding ways of expanding the pie that benefit themselves and the people around them," creating situations where "the whole is greater than the sum of the parts." When givers win, it "creates a ripple effect, enhancing the success of people around them." Mentorship creates a ripple effect, enhancing the success of people around them. Mentorship is an ultimate givers' game with investments into human capital creating synergistic learning and working environments and increasing the size of the pie for everyone involved. Although a mentor may not decide to begin mentoring for such future benefits, it is notable that this is a potential outcome, with former mentees offering a valued mentor positions on research teams, start-up companies, and so forth.[12] Mentors increase their impact upon future mentees through connecting mentees at various career stages thus increasing the number of development opportunities.

I wanted to give my mentee Sarah some writing experience, but no project was a good fit. Then, a former mentee, Jake, with whom I had worked with extensively a few years prior reached out. A journal invited had him to write a commentary. "The topic is the first thing we ever did together. Do you want to work together? Maybe you have a good student?" Thus, Jake gave me an opportunity to be an anchor author on an invited commentary but more importantly gave Sarah writing experience. I didn't help Jake originally thinking this situation would arise, but here we were: win-win-win.

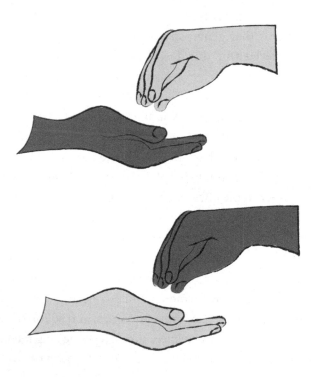

| MAXIM | Have mentors. |

Who Needs a Mentor (Or Why is Being a Mentee Important)?

Everyone needs a mentor. In fact, everyone needs more than one mentor. From advice to coaching to skill transfer to encouragement to new ideas to networking, we benefit more than we can ever pay back from mentors. That's why we are going to talk about paying it forward. Finding both professional success and personal satisfaction in a healthcare career and integrating those facets into a life characterized by wellness and fulfillment in the complex, everchanging world of modern medicine is a challenge insurmountable without the guidance, support, and experience of the well-meaning people that have come before us.

Who Needs a Mentee (Or Why is Being a Mentor Important)?

While we teach, we learn. – **Seneca**

Teaching fosters mastery of content because it inspires a teacher to achieve depth of understanding to break down complex concepts into easy to learn bites. Mentoring requires self-mastery: patience, empathy, insight, kindness, and self-knowledge. There are humbling, laugh at yourself moments when you're giving a mentee totally sound advice that you don't take yourself (e.g., when I advised a mentee not to email on weekends to improve work-life balance, and he politely pointed out I emailed him on Saturday).

Mentees can teach you new things and offer new ideas. I think of the time a mentee said, "Have you written a letter to the editor? I'd like to try that." My answer was, "No, I haven't, but we can learn together." This is a skill I have since passed on to other mentees, but the inspiration came from wanting to keep that mentee's fire kindled to be brave and curious and try new things (not to mention their great idea sparking the letter we wrote). Mentees will help you stay relevant, gain new perspective, and learn more about yourself.

What Does a Mentor Do?

Mentors hone a mentee's thought processes, problem-solving skills, and thinking tools. They widen perspectives, encourage trying new things, buoy confidence, act as soundboards, and generate food for thought. Mentors can help mentees think things they have never thought before. This environment helps a mentee to feel secure and supported, driving a mentee to take new risks to explore both their internal world as well as the external world of their life and career.

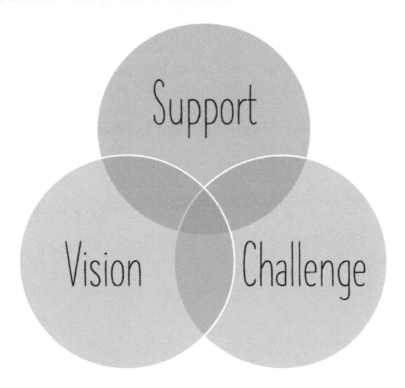

MENTORS PROVIDE SUPPORT, VISION, AND CHALLENGE

Support is provided through from the listening ear, verbalization of belief, and good advice. *Challenge* is created through setting high standards on "reach" tasks. *Vision* is generated, not only through enhanced self-aware-ness, but also giving mentees new ideas and breaking down self-imposed barriers that have shackled their potential.[13]

Vision

A mentor is someone who sees more talent and ability within you, than you see in yourself, and helps bring it out of you. – **Bob Proctor**

I remember distinctly the day my mentor said, "When you're a funded researcher..." I had never considered the possibility. I toyed with the idea, liking the sound of it and blushing at her belief in me. Another day, she said, "You could be President of that organization. Have you thought about it?" She gave me ideas I did not know I could have for myself and spoke with this belief in me that made me aim higher in my aspirations. Even though I didn't take her up on every grand idea she had for me, the discussions we had of how I could reach those goals and what those careers may look like was extremely beneficial.

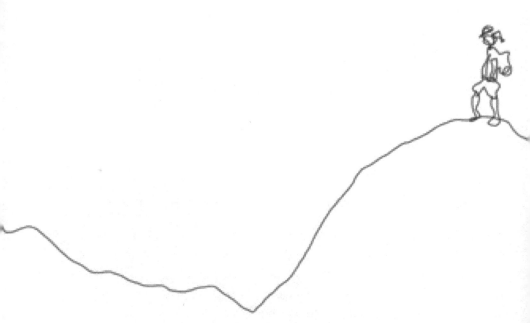

Most importantly (maybe... probably, let's be honest, thanks for: 1) your belief in me 2) speaking that belief into me. It is one thing to believe but another to go out of your way, kinda put yourself out there for the chance at me accepting the challenge. I really needed that and you knew that — so thanks.

A fourth-year student named Evan wrote me this note at the end of our 5-week rotation. Although extremely talented, his performance left something to be desired. During Feedback Friday, I challenged him: "I think you have more in you. I'm waiting for you to really surprise me with something. That's my challenge to you – show me what you've got. I hate this isn't more specific, but I'm looking for <u>more.</u>" He answered my challenge and then some, blowing me away with insight and productivity (he also surprised himself in this area). Beyond discussing critical care and academia topics, we dialogued a lot about what mattered in a career and in life. His note read: "Most importantly... thanks for: 1) your belief in me 2) speaking that belief into me. It is one thing to believe but another to go out of your way, kinda put yourself out there, for the chance at me accepting the challenge. I really needed that. And you knew that – so thanks."

Support

Having a caring, accomplished, and empathetic individual along the journey with you provides the emotional support to keep forging ahead and can make all the difference.

> *As a resident, I wanted to apply for a grant that required a recommendation from Patrick, my research advisor. I was nervous to ask because I knew he was busy, and we did not know each other well. I felt like an imposition. I worked up the courage and will never forget Patrick's immediate reaction: "Of course." Although soft spoken, he nearly interrupted me with this brisk, firm reply, as if wanting to dispel any doubts I had. His smile showed pride at my initiative. Patrick's response made me feel sheepish for not asking earlier, as if to say, "please never hesitate again." Those two words gave me support and connection that felt profound and invigorating. I was excited to keep trying because I had an advocate. You never know what kind smile or quickly jotted email will reach someone or may open a door for a new mentor-mentee relationship. Support comes in a myriad of forms (a listening ear, kind words, letters of recommendation, reviewing CVs and other products, advice, and so forth), but I have found that the simplest moments often mean the most. It has become one of my favorite moments in a day, if someone asks me for something, and I get to say, "Of course."*

Mostly, though, support comes from the empowering feeling that there is someone that cares for you and believes in you. In a wonderfully written article in *The Atlantic*, Larry Hall recalled the words of Jean Rhodes, one of the nation's leading experts on mentoring: *If you talk to successful people about what made a difference in their lives, it often comes down to the involvement of a caring adult over time and during critical moments.*

Challenge

---

*Challenges are what make life interesting; overcoming
them is what makes life meaningful. –* **Joshua J. Marine**

In *Seabiscuit*, Laura Hillenbrand recounts the rehabilitation of the horse
that led him to become a champion. After years of mishandling, the
horse's natural competitor's instinct had been turned away from running
to fighting the jockey: ". . . asked him for speed, the horse slowed down . . .
asked to go left, he'd dodge right; tugged right, he'd dart left." Trainer Tom
Smith gave a different command; "Let him go." The whip was put away,
and he was given a structured, caring environment. "Once he was no longer
being coerced, his instincts bubbled back to the surface. His innate love
of running returned." Seabiscuit would go on to be one of the most celebrated horses in history.

The type of individual that chooses a healthcare career is often one
with strong work ethic and a desire to give back to others (their version
of Seabiscuit's innate love of running). With their love of learning and
desire to give back, they are fueled by mastering challenges in the broader
context of helping others. Mentors have a unique opportunity to guide
and energize this innate drive by supporting and validating these characteristics as well as sponsoring them with the right races to run. Sometimes,
reminding mentees of these traits is enough to rekindle the flames. Mentors
are encouraged to reframe work-related activities in the mentee's eyes: opportunities that broaden experience and skillsets.

> *In the course of conversation with my mentee, Kate, I said I needed
> to write quiz questions that I had forgotten were due. Kate asked
> if she could help, and I decided to take her up on the offer. She did
> wonderfully. By the end, I was not sure who was thanking who. She
> loved the challenge of "seeing quiz questions from the other side,"
> and beyond her enormous help meeting a deadline, I felt renewed
> as an educator by her enthusiasm to take on a new challenge.*

*Life is about accepting the challenges
along the way, choosing to
keep moving forward, and
savoring the journey.* – **Roy T. Bennett**

A Journey with Many Guides

Mentors are not the only type of person involved in the journey of professional development. Different individuals will play a variety of roles, each with unique objectives. Notably, these roles may overlap.

Professor – An individual employed by an institution of higher learning with multiple roles (e.g., educator, scientist) most frequently encountered during degree training

Preceptor – A teacher or instructor encountered in the experiential, clinical environment. Often, this individual is employed full-time as a clinician and oversees trainees as part of their practice site

Coach – An individual with experience in teaching who focuses on developing a specific skillset through training, guidance, and opportunities for practice

Manager – An individual employed to supervise a group of employees to progress the mission of the organization

Advisor – An individual assigned within a structured program who assists the advisee in planning and achieving their course of study or continued education

Role Model – An individual who displays a certain standard of excellence that inspires imitation because of their positive professional and/or personal characteristics; a source of inspiration

Sponsor – An accomplished, well-positioned, and well-connected individual who can use their influence to facilitate a protégé's entry and advancement in the field through recommendations, network connections, and opportunities. Sponsors actively look for good opportunities for their sponsee. Sponsors may be considered the highest level of commitment and trust because the sponsor is "sticking their neck out" for the sponsee

Mentor – An active partner in an ongoing relationship defined by a commitment to mutual growth and shared altruism with the goal to maximize and realize the mentee's professional and personal potential

Build a Mentorship Team

*We are the average of the five people
we spend the most time with.* – **John Rohn**

MYTH: You can only have (and only need) one mentor.

Taken together, these different guides create a beautifully connected web of individuals, with mentorship driving the qualities of mutual growth and shared altruism. These networks can enhance feelings of belonging and support but also play on the classical proverb: "It takes a village to raise a child." So too, it takes a healthcare community to train a responsible and caring healthcare professional. Mentees are encouraged to have multiple mentors that fulfill different needs.

One-on-One Mentorship

Also called "traditional" mentorship, this is the type of mentorship most people think of when they hear about mentorship. This is a one-on-one relationship between a more senior individual (the mentor) and a more junior individual (the mentee).

"Just in Time" or "Focused" Mentorship

In a healthcare career, there are times when a specific new skill or a difficult scenario require a content expert. In these cases, individuals with or without an existing relationship may pair together for a targeted, discrete experience. These interactions require all of the best practices of mentorship (e.g., active listening, confidentiality, altruism, etc.) but may not include relationship longevity or high outputs of commitment between the two individuals. For example, when navigating promotion, my existing mentors were not as familiar with this process, so I reached out for consultation and support for developing my dossier. This individual gave me candid and confidential advising and shared in my celebration upon receiving a positive review, but it is not a relationship that we actively maintain on a regular basis.

Group Mentorship

A small group can provide a powerful form of mentorship. Usually, these groups have targeted foci and meet on a regular schedule. Agendas can improve quality of the discussions but just as important is the "free discussion" period. At one point in my career, I found myself without many peers in my profession and discipline also interested in federal funding. Floundering with the difficulty of grant writing and its foreignness compared to clinical training, I reached out to identify people who might share my experience. We formed a group that met quarterly, dubbed the "K-Team" (in honor of pursuing K-training grants). We also joked it was a grant writing support group. Having other trusted individuals share my exact frustrations and doubts, while also giving sound advice, has been invaluable.

Reverse Mentoring

"Everyone has something to teach you if you are humble enough to learn," says Mark Driscoll. Though mentorship is traditionally viewed in a hierarchical manner, with the more experienced individual transferring knowledge to the more junior person, there is much to be gained for flipping this construct on its head! Especially in the age of rapid technology innovation that favors the younger generation, realizing that everyone can teach you something yields numerous benefits. Often touted as a separate construct, it is *foundational* to high-quality mentorship. Both mentees and mentors should be on the lookout for opportunities to share their unique experiences and skills and participate in the "give and take" of mentorship.

> *Even as a Millennial who supposedly absorbs new technology with ease, my mentees have taught me new smartphone tricks, from sharing a location to scanning PDF files. It was a mentee who said that I might enjoy bicycle riding given my love of nature, uninterrupted thinking time, and exercising. He ad-*

vised me on buying my first bike off Craigslist. I loved when my bargain deal was praised by the local bike shop for being "hand-made in Japan, truly a work of art. This bike has soul." This hobby has become one of my favorite parts of the day (and indeed, the idea for this book occurred while biking). I collect magnets in my office from places that I've traveled. A mentee of mine pointed to a magnet from Vietnam and said, "You took your students to Thai last week? I think you like Asian cuisine. In Chinese culture, it would be an honor to cook for you. I could teach you how to make dumplings?" And so we celebrated his residency match by me learning how to make traditional, hand-folded dumplings, an amazing experience. Then, another student heard of this story, and said, "Have you had inarizushi before?" I said no, and he explained it was rice in a fried tofu package, which sounded delightful. I insisted that I was happy to meet without food-related incentives, but he shared, "In my culture, it is easier to talk over food, and to show gratitude to someone helping. It would mean a lot to me." And so again, I found myself enjoying a new culinary and cultural experience in my office while discussing his career aspirations. Mentees consistently expand my horizons.

Peer Mentoring

Peer mentoring occurs when two individuals are at a similar career stage, especially in an early career phase or a highly transitional mid-career phase.[14] With regard to general years of experience, skillsets, and achievements, the individuals are approximate equals. Key advantages include increasing access to many of the benefits of mentorship (overcoming potential capacity limits of senior mentors) and psychosocial benefits that may include emotional support and working partnerships leading to "deliverables." It may even be related to retention of early career professionals, especially in academic healthcare settings. These relationships may have the potential to remove a more toxic, competitive environment and focus on how to promote the other individual and maximize the relationship. This may also encompass "step-ahead" mentoring, where an individual is just beyond one's current place and provides highly relevant advice.

Examples of Peer Mentoring Activities or Habits Include

- Sponsoring an activity that you've already completed (e.g., passing along the invitation to peer-review for a journal you have already peer-reviewed)

- Completing "pro-bono" peer review of deliverable products (e.g., educational materials, promotion packets)

- Nominating each other for various awards relevant to the profession (tip: Having a "template" letter or personal bio for the other individual already established can make this process easier)

- Regular meetings to discuss work that also include a social aspect

Tips and Tricks for Developing High Quality Peer Mentors

- Find individuals with similar values and goals

- Be generous and proactive in offering to review materials, provide nominations, etc.

- Schedule face time (the power of the "working lunch" cannot be undersold in these scenarios)

Shared joy is double joy;
Shared sorrow is half a sorrow. – **Swedish Proverb**

Layered Mentoring and Mentorship Networks

A senior mentor can create meaningful development opportunities and new topics for discussion through fostering layered mentoring. *Layered learning* is a teaching methodology employed in healthcare education where more experienced trainees coach less experienced trainees under the supervision of a preceptor and is employed both in the clinical and research setting.[15] A resident overseeing a student complete a medication history with the resident providing feedback to the student and the preceptor providing feedback to the resident on their coaching style is an example. Mentors can employ layered mentoring in a similar fashion by having more senior mentees provide feedback on a curriculum vitae or encouraging mentees to meet. Not only does this practice promote meaningful networks, but it can also provide opportunities for mentees to practice new mentoring skillsets (e.g., how to provide feedback).

In *My Reading Life*,[16] Pat Conroy recalls how his first mentor, a high school English teacher, would set up interviews with current students after he became a bestselling author. It was apparent how much time the student and his mentor had spent preparing for the interview. The learning came both from the interview and the preparation.

"It's not what you know but who you know" is a common adage that bespeaks to the power of social capital. Social capital, in form of the mentor/mentee relationship, is a key benefit, but mentors can also catapult a mentee forward by facilitating connections. For example, a mentor and colleague of mine named Jack connected me with his mentee, Rebecca: "She is a great student and has some similar interests to you. I feel like you two would hit it off." Rebecca and I talked for an hour, and a new connection in our network was born. This "delegated mentoring" connects mentees with mentors best suited for their needs. Visualizing yourself as part of a large, diverse community of mentors and mentees and creatively thinking about how to link these individuals can increase community.

Synergizing in a Team Environment

Mentors can enhance the experience they provide by synergizing three constructs: *mentorship networks, layered learning, and team science.*[17] Recognized by the National Institutes of Health as "a collaborative effort to address a scientific challenge that leverages the strengths and expertise of professionals trained in different fields," team science is analogous to multiprofessional teams known as the gold standard for patient care.[18] Integrating mentees into existing teams and applying principles of layered learning and mentorship networks can create productive, caring environments tailored to healthcare trainees. Simon Sinek writes, "The true value of networking doesn't come from how many people we can meet but rather how many people we can introduce to others."

> *When I started as a new faculty member, I had the good fortune to join four other faculty into what has becoming a very high functioning team (our slogan has become 'teamwork makes the dream work'). This team has been a prime environment for us with regard to peer, step ahead, traditional, and reverse mentoring. More importantly, it's created a 'village' for our trainees. This has been incredible synergy, and I encourage this strategy whenever possible.*

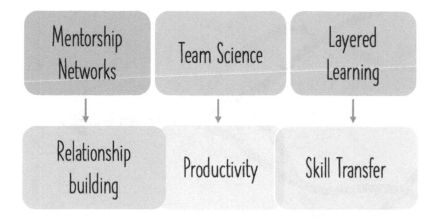

Integrate, don't create

A classic mentor mistake is to create new projects for a mentee instead of integrating mentees into ongoing projects. This practice divides a mentor's time and effort as opposed to streamlining their efforts and even allowing the mentee to serve as an extender. For example, if the mentor's priority is to complete institutional quality improvement project on the use of neuromuscular blockade, a mentee's project could be completing an audit about current practices or analyzing existing data. This would be integration. In contrast, creating new work would be to have the mentee do an unrelated project on antibiotics. Mentoring in conjunction with career related priorities helps the mentor to have bandwidth for an appropriate level of investment. Although situations arise where a mentee is relatively autonomous and a separate project may be desirable, this practice should be carefully scrutinized and deliberately undertaken.

My personal practice is to look for a way to incorporate mentees into a vast majority of my work (e.g., journal reviews, abstracts, manuscripts, presentations, etc.). Although, at times, this adds extra layers of effort for me, the learning opportunities are invaluable to pass along. Moreover, my general rule is not to create new work just because a mentee wants a project. Integration into existing work aligns multiple priorities at once.

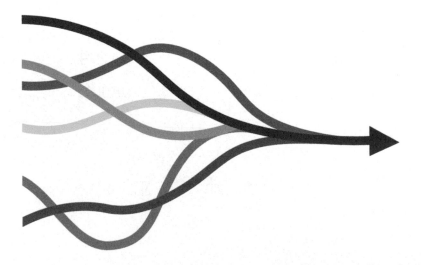

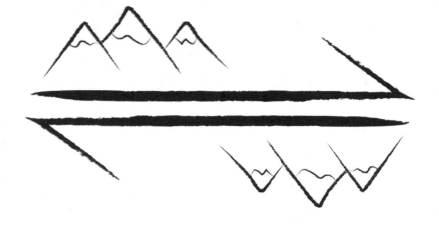

2

MENTORSHIP MINDSETS

This section will focus on the mindsets, attitudes, and beliefs of high-quality mentorship.

Relationships as the Medium for Growth

In art, a medium is defined as the substances used by the artist to create a piece of artwork. For example, oil paints on canvas or charcoal on paper would be mediums. The artist uses the medium to develop the final work. Using this metaphor in mentorship, the "medium" is the relationship itself. The artists are the mentee and mentor, co-creators of the final product. The final product is personal growth or other goal achievement. Thus, participation in the relationship is of their own volition. It becomes the tool through which the mentor and mentee grow. Similarly, good relationships are like higher-quality paints, which yield better products.

Ideal mentor-mentee relationships cultivate a safe space for trial and error, exploration of new ideas, and self-reflection. Creating this secure, creative space demands that each individual bring their best self to the table. Adam Grant defines psychological safety as "the belief that you can take a risk without being penalized or punished."[11] The feeling of being seen and this sense of security fuels courage to take risks and try out new attitudes and experiences.

Dialogue is the basis of the relationship. High-quality dialogue directly affects the strength of the relationship and thus the potential for mutual growth and fulfillment. Actively strategizing how to enhance dialogue is well worth the effort. This book provides an introduction to these concepts but books like *Power Mentoring*[12] and *10 Steps to Successful Mentoring*[19] provide expanded discussion and step-by-step guides for meetings, agendas, and questions to ask.

Growth Mindset

In *Mindset*[20], Carol Dweck explains how individuals energized (as opposed to discouraged) by challenges, setbacks, and criticism often go on to be more successful due to a growth mindset.

> *"In a growth mindset," she explains, "people believe that their most basic abilities can be developed through dedication and hard work—brains and talent are just the starting point. This view creates a love of learning and a resilience that is essential for great accomplishment."*

Helping mentees adopt and reinforce this mindset is a key role for mentors. Mentors help mentees reframe negative feedback and other setbacks as valuable learning opportunities and chances for self-reflection. Mentors also encourage mentees to take on challenging tasks and praise their effort over the specific result.

"Feedback Friday" is a common practice with trainees on clinical rotations, but many times "feedback" denotes a negative connotation. In my experience, trainees often show up for this touchpoint worried about hearing all the things they messed up and are surprised to answer these four key questions instead:

1. What went well this week?

2. What are you most proud of this week?

3. What do you want to focus on next week for your next steps?

4. How can we make that next step happen?

We celebrate successes and hard work and strategize about the rest of the rotation: what we should focus on and how we should go about it (our game plan). Although weak points and areas for development are discussed, we discuss these in a positive light and as a team. It is music to my ears to hear "how challenging and fun this rotation was." Being outside your comfort zone is good.

MAXIM	Cultivate "no ego" (or a growth and servant-oriented mindset).

Wisdom

Mentors help translate knowledge into wisdom. Ignorance may be defined as "not knowing what you don't know." Being respectful of your own ignorance and things 'you do not know that you don't know' is a key reason to have mentors. The Johari Window has been proposed to explain this concept. The window has four quadrants: open (known to self and others), hidden (known to self and not to others), blind spot (not known to self but known to others), and unknown (not known to anyone). A mentor can help specifically to reduce personal blind spots.

In a story of Socrates, the Delphic Oracle tells Socrates' friend that Socrates is the wisest man alive. Socrates responds by trying to prove the Oracle wrong. He embarks on a quest interrogating everyone he meets to find someone wiser. In the end, he concludes, "I am wiser than this man; it is likely that neither of us knows anything worthwhile, but he thinks he knows something when he does not, whereas when I do not know, neither do I think I know, so I am likely to be wiser than he to this small extent, that I do not think I know what I do not know."

Personally, I have to come view all higher education as embarking upon a journey of learning more clearly all that one does not know. Even a medication so simple as acetaminophen still has a mechanism of action not entirely understood by the scientific community. This is the joy of higher learning: realizing that wisdom is simply knowing that you know very little at all. Mentors often help open your eyes to this process.

The Johari Window Model (adapted to right) has been proposed as a means of understanding the relationship of ourselves to others has been adapted for medical education.[21]

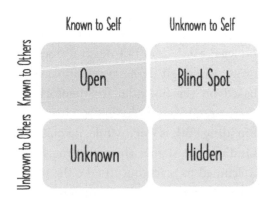

Mentorship: A Deliberate Practice

MYTH: Mentorship is informal. Anyone can do it, and it doesn't take any particular skill or practice to do.

Mentorship is a deliberate practice. It takes active effort to develop the skillsets needed to be an effective mentor, and it takes time to create meaningful, long-lasting relationships. While everyone is capable of being in a mentorship relationship, it will not come without overt effort to develop emotional intelligence, empathetic listening, and other relevant psychosocial skills.

Importantly, the banner of "mentorship" can be misused, with individuals quick to tell people what to do, touting zealous opinions, and serving their own interests under the guise of being a guide to someone else. This is not mentorship.

Mentorship is unlikely just to happen without intentionality. Self-reflection on goals, identifying relationships worth cultivating, and nurturing those relationships takes effort. However, the relationship itself should feel organic and unforced. To many, being asked, "Will you be my mentor?" during a first meeting is an uncomfortable question because mentorship requires mutual commitment. How can either person know if it is a good fit? Like other meaningful relationships, the best mentorship relationships take time to nurture and often feel like they just fell into place.

However, simply because the relationship is informal, in that there is no legal bind, does not mean it does not require effort to maintain and grow. Although *de novo* relationships, wherein interaction is expressly based on the potential for mentoring relationship, are possible, likely, there are already individuals with whom you have a shared connection. Pursuing both is worthwhile. Be on the lookout for natural spark but then kindle those flames through time spent together. Potential mentors are welcomed to reach out to take the next step as well, if they see someone with whom they feel they can connect or help.

Mentorship as an Infinite Game

One can never pay in gratitude: one can only pay "in kind" somewhere else in life. – **Anne Morrow Lindbergh**

With an education funded by student loans, I clearly remember a professor and mentor named Elizabeth taking me to a fancy Italian restaurant and my gratitude for that good meal. More so, the conversation, where we talked about her career, opened my eyes to so many possibilities. I thanked her, and she said, "Just remember to take students to lunch someday They're all hungry, and they'll never forget it." Another time, we sat together while she edited my writing, walking me through the construction of the paper. I remember thinking "she could have done this without me in a quarter of the time, but I wouldn't have learned anything. How can I ever say thank you enough?" Mentorship is a gift that is impossible to pay back, but as Catherine Ryan Hyde says, "If you can't pay it back, pay it forward." Mentorship teaches us to be grateful and gracious receivers, and in turn, it can provide a source of inspiration towards professional generosity.

An adage attributed to Peter Drucker says, "What gets measured, gets managed." If something is important, finding a way to measure it will allow for meaningful evaluation. Does mentorship have a metric? Some metrics, depending on practice area, may be important for annual reviews like "number of trainees that completed residency or fellowship" or "number of trainees that were authors on abstracts and manuscripts." Even jotting down the number of recommendation letters can be useful, but these fail to capture the more holistic, altruistic reasons that inspire us to mentor.

The truest metric of mentorship success is how many mentors that person makes, how many people did they inspire to 'pay it forward.' In *The Infinite Game*, Simon Sinek discusses how "infinite games have no finish line and the goal is to keep the game going as long as possible."[22]

Mentorship can be viewed as an Infinite Game, where we adopt the "Just Cause" (something that we believe is bigger than ourselves) and identify our "why" as keeping the legacy of mentorship alive and thriving.[22] In the Infinite Game of mentorship, our Just Cause is Paying It Forward. Our metric is making mentors.

| MAXIM | Pay it forward. |

Your Why

Everyone will have a unique why. It is vital for mentors and mentees to identify their "why."

| MAXIM | Identify your why. |

Responsibility and Commitment

Mentors can have great power over a mentee's mindset and career. As mentors, be humble and mindful of this influence. As a mentor, you will be carefully (if covertly) studied for your work habits, your attitudes, how you handle being under pressure, how you deal with setbacks, your professionalism, your commitment to patients and trainees, and even your foibles. One time, I was told a story of my own quirks as a means of recognizing me in the classroom:

> *My mentee, Bart, asked, "Do you know Andrea?" The student replied, "No, I don't think so." Bart said, "She's the one that has ChapStick and a sparkling water, like, everywhere she goes." The student said, "Oh yeah! I know her!"*

It can be easy to forget what it was like to be in training and the days when you didn't know all the ropes. Whether you know it or not, you may very well be a role model and source of inspiration to another person. Being a mentor means accepting this mantle. This power should be undertaken with a servant's mindset. First coined by Robert K. Greenleaf in a 1970 essay, he writes:

> *The servant-leader is servant first… It begins with the natural feeling that one wants to serve, to serve first. Then conscious choice brings one to aspire to lead. That person is sharply different from one who is leader first, perhaps because of the need to assuage an unusual power drive or to acquire material possessions…The difference manifests itself in the care taken by the servant-first to make sure that other people's highest priority needs are being served. The best test, and difficult to administer, is: Do those served grow as persons? Do they, while being served, become healthier, wiser, freer, more autonomous, more likely themselves to become servants? What is the effect on the least privileged in society? Will they benefit?* [3]

To foster mutual growth and shared altruism, to guide another person on their own journey of self-fulfillment, means accepting a profound level of responsibility and commitment. Being a mentor should never be taken lightly. Moreover, we are accepting a commitment to develop our best selves as well, which enriches the mentee's experience. Clear structure, commitment, and ethics govern the integrity of mentorship. Mentorship is a cornerstone to healthcare delivery: deliberately taking responsibility for this rich legacy has powerful ramifications for the care and education we provide.

What does that mean 'tame'?

"It is an act too often neglected, said the fox, it means 'to establish ties.'"

..."People have forgotten this truth," the fox said, "But you mustn't forget it. You become responsible forever for what you've tamed." – **Antoine de Saint-Exupéry, *The Little Prince***

Mentorship Ethics

Healthcare ethics has been proposed as a construct for healthcare mentorship.[23,24] Healthcare ethics (or "medical ethics") is an applied branch of ethics that focuses on the moral principles, beliefs, and values that guide healthcare professionals and policymakers alike as we make choices regarding medical care. Ethics attempts to codify our core sense of right and wrong, delineate what we believe regarding the rights as human beings we all possess, and understand the duties we owe to others.

In healthcare ethics, respecting dignity by seeking to honor a patient's right to make their own decisions (autonomy), helping the patient seek their own benefit (beneficence), vowing not to harm a patient (nonmaleficence), treating patients fairly (justice), and speaking with honesty (truthfulness) are the guiding principles.

Here are the definitions and how they apply to mentorship:

Beneficence – The goal is net benefit for the individuals involved, especially the success of the mentee.

Truthfulness – A mentoring relationship is a personal relationship characterized by trust. Trust has been defined as "choosing to risk making something you value vulnerable to another person's actions."[25] Core to trust-building is honesty, in combination with empathy, consistency, and respect for dignity. T.S. Eliot writes, "Those who trust us, educate us."

Justice – The intent that the burdens and benefits should be distributed equally and equitably among individuals (i.e., mentor and mentee).

Nonmaleficence – The intent that actions are undertaken without harm to any individual (the combination of beneficence and non-maleficence makes up shared altruism, a defining characteristic of mentorship).

Autonomy – Collective respect for the independence of thoughts, intentions, opinions, and actions of both mentor and mentee.

Autonomy

Mindset

Independent, successful functioning of the mentee is the ultimate goal.

Mentor Actions	Mentee Actions
✏ Identify challenging (but still attainable) activities	✏ Seek alternative viewpoints regularly
✏ Engage mentees in dialogue that explores their thought processes	✏ Provide follow-up on guidance received
✏ Respect differences of opinion and when a mentee chooses not to follow advice	✏ Be clear about which advice is and is not taken
✏ Keep high standards	✏ Openly participate in meaningful dialogue

Mentors must be mindful of micromanaging mentee projects or never letting the mentee fail or face disappointment. Mentees must recognize the need for alternative mentorship. Both must be thoughtful of the progression through the stages of mentorship and view this transition to independence as a mutual success.

Best Practice: Explain Why

Providing context and reasons for the importance of a project is not only a classic means of generating 'buy-in' from mentees but also a valuable means to enhance their autonomy and decision-making.

One time, I was telling Margaret, a mentee, about a journal review that was due soon. She asked if she could be involved. I said, "I would have asked you, but you've done these before; you'd be more just doing work for me than necessarily learning a new skill." Margaret thought about it and then said, "This is a topic I don't know much about but would like to know more. Plus, you've helped me a lot, I'd enjoy spending some time on it." This practice of openness was empowering for Margaret to decide and maybe even deepened our relationship, that it felt more like a two-way street with her helping me. Other times, I've explained my rationale and mentees decide to go a different direction: these are important moments for learning about each other.

Beneficence

Mindset

Beneficence is defined as the act of doing good, charity, or kindness. The goal of a mentoring relationship is the personal and professional success of the mentee.

Mentor Actions	Mentee Actions
✿ Identify new connections or individuals based on mentee interests	✿ Honor assignments with excellent quality work products
✿ Provide support and encouragement and capture moments worthy of celebration	✿ Generate new ideas and discussions with the mentor
✿ Suggest reading materials or opportunities for new learning	✿ Provide meaningful feedback on activities and mentorship style
✿ Carefully evaluate return on investment for all suggested activities	✿ View the relationship as a reflection of each other professionally

"Going easy" on someone is often mistaken for kindness, but beneficence is just as much giving tough feedback and assigning difficult tasks as it is celebrating success. Mentors must be careful not to let inertia stall identifying the next steps for a mentee and keep their best interests at the forefront.

> *Once, my mom was reflecting on being a parent: "Oftentimes, as a mom, the thing I felt was most important was for you to feel loved and to give you the resources you needed, be that construction paper or soccer shoes. It felt like you'd do the rest." In some ways, mentorship is much the same: provide support and resources and be a source of encouragement to your mentees. Your mentees will do the rest.*

A candle loses nothing by lighting another candle. – **James Keller**

Justice

Mindset

Justice concerns the equitable distribution of benefits and burdens across individuals. It may be thought of as fair treatment of individuals and equitable allocation of resources. In mentorship, it deals with respecting each other's time, resources, person, and professional identity.

Mentor Actions	Mentee Actions
✿ Dividing shared work meaningfully, with priority placed on learning experiences and mentee time ✿ Prioritizing time to provide high-quality sessions regarding advice, feedback, and dialogue	✿ Committing appropriate effort towards assigned activities ✿ Respecting the mentor's advice and attempting to apply it, as is reasonable

The biggest challenge faced by mentors and mentees in honoring the principle of justice is avoiding over-commitments that result in failure to place appropriate time and effort into the relationship as well as associated work products. Careful evaluation of commitments is essential, and touch points regarding bandwidth are normal dimensions to high-quality mentorship.

Although it can be difficult to turn down a mentee, it is a better practice to be clear about current bandwidth than to accept a role on a study team or project and not deliver on those commitments. Ghosting a mentee on a project can lead to significant project-related setbacks and also degradation of the relationship.

Best Practice: Finish the Drill

Anyone who has ever had a project fizzle out can relate to the frustration of lost time and maybe feelings of abandonment. In thinking of justice, one of my maxims is "finish the drill" when it comes to mentees and projects (i.e., finding some way to translate work done into a deliverable on their CV, etc.), regardless of shifted priorities or passions.

Non-Maleficence

Mindset

All interactions of a healthy mentor-mentee relationship must be taken with the best interests of the mentee at the heart.

Mentors must be cognizant that they also hold an authority position with regard to title (e.g., professor, program director) or stature associated with professional reputation. This uneven power dynamic can be both intentionally and unintentionally used to the detriment of the mentee. Early warning signs include not providing appropriate credit to work products, assigning work that is to the primary benefit of the mentor and not the mentee, and other types of coercion or harassment.

Mentor Actions	Mentee Actions
• Carefully review the time investment versus benefit for all suggested experiences/assignments • Provide the appropriate level of credit for all works • Avoid harmful or other mean-spirited comments	• Awareness that professional products completed together are a mutual representation of each individual • Seek outside counsel in the situation where shared altruism is not present

A *senna* plant

People are like plants: they grow towards the light. – **Hope Jahren**

Truthfulness

Authenticity is a collection of choices that we have to make every day. It's about the choice to show up and be real. The choice to be honest. The choice to let our true selves be seen. – **Brené Brown**

Mindset

Mutual growth requires honesty. From bi-directional feedback to thoughtful self-disclosure, being vulnerable is directly associated with courage, creativity, and self-love. Mentoring relationships can be excellent places to practice such openness. Embrace honesty as an ultimate form of kindness. Failure to have difficult conversations for poor performance can lead to resentment. Never use revelations as a form of emotional blackmail but as a springboard to further exploration. Warren Buffet says, "Honesty is a very expensive gift; just don't expect it from cheap people." In this way, some of the greatest value of the relationship is in its honesty tempered by kindness.

Mentor Actions	Mentee Actions
🍂 Schedule time for open dialogue and ask difficult questions 🍂 Provide detailed but kind feedback at regular intervals (positive and negative)	🍂 Reflect on questions and discussions for future conversations 🍂 Be honest regarding current struggles, feelings, commitments

In *Power Mentoring*[12], one mentor-protégé relationship discussed how they served these roles for each other: "Guardian of conscience, Sounding Board, Truth teller." These roles demanded that each individual refine their beliefs and values and then to live authentically towards them. Their story is a potent reminder of the value of honesty.

However, as I felt the blow my only thought was truth. Does truth come in blows? – **Saul Bellow**

Cheerleaders and Celebrators

The most beautiful things are not associated with money; they are memories and moments. If you don't celebrate those, they can pass you by. – Alek Wek

---

Cheerleaders genuinely believe in you and make that belief known. They are sincere in their positive remarks and shows of affirmation: "You are capable of that, if you want to." They say, "I believe you can get better" at setbacks because their belief in you goes beyond short-term outcomes.

Imposter Syndrome (wherein a collection of feelings of inadequacy persist despite evidence of success) can be combatted with people who both know you well and see your potential. Similar to Elbert Hubbard when he described a friend as "someone who knows all about you and still loves you," a mentor is someone who knows all about you and still believes in you full-heartedly.

A career in healthcare is filled with delayed gratification (graduate degrees, promotion and tenure, and board certification all take years to achieve). Taking time to celebrate these milestones together not only fosters the relationship and can increase feelings of connection but is a vital time for gratitude and joy. Celebrating successes encourages a growth mindset that honors sustained effort. It can become too easy to see the dedication and time needed to have success in the field as normal through comparing yourself to immediate peers instead of realizing the level of achievement is significant. Helping a mentee see their success in a broader context is time well spent.

When I got my dream job as a professor, my long-time mentor, Elizabeth, took me to dinner. We toasted champagne and ate Italian (a bit of a tradition since that first meal as a student). I loved basking in that moment. I returned the favor upon her retirement, where I cooked pesto pasta, and we once again toasted champagne while watching the sunset, reminiscing, and chatting. I also recall the quiet knock on my door from one of my more soft-spoken mentees, Jake, to tell me our paper had been accepted. Later, Jake told me how much it meant to him to see me jump up from behind my desk to give him a pound and ask if he had time to get coffee to celebrate. Having someone recognize your efforts is a key means to wanting to keep going, even when the journey is hard.

Remember to celebrate the milestones as you prepare ahead. – **Nelson Mandela**

Gratitude

Acknowledging the good that you already have in your life is the foundation for all abundance. – **Eckhart Tolle**

Practicing an "attitude of gratitude" is well established to improve your sense of wellbeing, happiness, and community.[26] Overt practices of gratitude in day-to-day life include the act of thanking others, journaling, or scheduling specific time for reflection. Fostering gratitude within the mentorship context can deepen relationships and foster awareness of the value brought by each individual.

Mentors can encourage mentees to practice gratitude in their professional life through thanking preceptors, advisors, and co-workers. Mentors can also make a practice of thanking mentees for their ideas and effort. The power of the handwritten note cannot be undersold and many an educator will pull out a file of thank you notes collected over the years saying something like, "I read these when I'm having a bad day." Mentorship is as an act of service that we can be grateful for.

Pictured: *A hand-painted thank you note from a mentee quoting Rumi (one of my favorites), in honor of a day spent at a conference working on various projects together.*

The more you praise and celebrate your life, the more there is to celebrate. – **Oprah Winfrey**

Fostering a One-on-One Relationship

The power of mentorship lies in the strength of the relationship between the two individuals. Engaging in a series of authentic practices to strengthen the relationship is well worth the investment. What you invest in the relationship will be what you get back.

Build Trust	High-Quality Communication
✍ Consider meetings out of the office, like walking together and sharing coffee or meals ✍ Appropriate self-disclosure practices sharing experiences on receiving difficult feedback, overcoming challenging setbacks, and current career success ✍ Openly discuss strengths and provide reassurance ✍ Encourage questions ("no such thing as a bad question") and attempt to give thoughtful answers	✍ High-quality interpersonal communication practices (e.g., active listening, receptive body language) ✍ Thoughtfully asking open-ended questions on topics that may be worth exploring ✍ Gentle confrontation to encourage thoughts about difficult issues in a non-judgmental way (e.g., pointing out apparent discrepancies between words and actions to identify new insights)

The research that meaningful, out-of-classroom interactions between faculty and students improves learning and performance is so compelling that university funds have been allocated to support this type of activity as a means of enhancing the higher education experience.[6] Breaking bread together is a powerful form of community and relationship building that should not be undersold. Regardless, mentors and mentees are encouraged to find ways to have high-quality interactions to foster a meaningful one-on-one relationship. "Tests" that deepen relationship including mentees following through on assignments and navigating situations with emotional intelligence, gratitude, and honesty.

"What I'm really concerned about is reaching one person." – **Jorge Luis Borges**

Creating a Conversational Safe Space

Without safety, no risk taking can occur. Without risk, no growth can occur. The defining feature of successful mentoring relationships is the development of a secure zone that serves as the basis of future creative and growth-oriented efforts. *A conversational safe space is essential in mentorship.* Only when mentees feel safe to disclose and explore will any true work begin, and a big mistake mentors can make is assuming mentees feel safe. Safe spaces are defined by mutual trust and respect and are created through high-quality interactions where each individual is fully present with the other, listening with open minds and full hearts, asking thought-provoking questions, and co-creating plans. Creating this space comes through dialogue together.

This type of description may sound like a soup of buzzwords and other jargon, but it is no easy undertaking; creating such a space takes discipline (to withhold judgement, to keep wandering attention spans at bay), self-awareness (only honed through deliberate effort), and targeted deployment of relationship building practices.

In the right environment where they feel heard, a mentee is capable of expanding their horizons and thinking in new ways, delving deep into reflection with meaningful self-disclosure, and breaking old habits and creating new. Safe spaces forge courage. Thus, this is one of the greatest dichotomies: braving the unknown is often best done when starting from a known place of security. Yet another dichotomy, you want your mentee to feel safe with you so that they manage the feelings of lack of safety and cultivate courage as they take on new challenges. Having a trusted and respected individual sign off on a new endeavor—validating its worth, believing in its feasibility—can make all the difference.

On the Value of Meaningful Dialogue

Our chief want is someone who will inspire us to be what we know we could be. – **Ralph Waldo Emerson**

Meaningful dialogue is the foundation of a high-quality mentoring relationship. Cal Newport writes that "face-to-face conversation is the most human—and humanizing—thing we do. Fully present to one another, we learn to listen. It's where we develop the capacity for empathy. It's where we experience the joy of being heard, of being understood."[27]

Indeed, Pat Conroy describes "real conversation" as having "an unpredictability, danger, and resonance." Real conversation can "take a turn anywhere and constantly borders on the unexpected and on the unknown. Real conversation is not a construct of the solitary ego; it creates community."

Jordan Peterson writes that "genuine conversation is exploration, articulation, and strategizing. When you're involved in genuine conversation, you're listening, and talking, but mostly listening. Listening is paying attention." He goes on to describe in *12 Rules for Life*[28] a conversation style called mutual exploration. He says this approach "assumes both parties come to the table without preconceived notions of being right, allowing the dialogue to repair and improve its structure, and expand its domain." At the end, he injuncts, "Assume that the person you are listening to knows something you don't." This type of dialogue is powerful, and it is unsurprising that psychosocial research demonstrates that through dialogue, we can have direct effects on a person's neuro-functioning.[19]

When conversation and dialogue are described in this manner, it becomes clear why they are so essential to mentorship. A core purpose of a mentor is self-discovery, and one of the most powerful ways to learn about yourself is in the context of meaningful dialogue. This dialogue relies on making face time for conversation and active listening during that time. Active listening is a form of engaged listening characterized by non-judgement, curiosity, patience, thoughtful silences, asking questions, reflecting back what has been said, asking for clarification or summarizing, and effective use of verbal and non-verbal feedback to communicate your attention. Building psychological safety is fundamental to this experience, as this sets up the foundation upon which mentees can fully embrace the rigors of growth.

Practical tips for maximizing this important practice include blocking appropriate time for wandering conversation and putting away distractions. Engaging in this activity while walking or over coffee or a meal can facilitate focus. While other meetings may be focused on specific tasks (e.g., CV review) or topics like interview prep, time must be specifically allocated for this important facet of relationship and trust building. Put simply, it takes time to get to know someone, especially time after both people feel comfortable with each other to show more and more of their true selves. This time is invaluable.

Questioning with curiosity

Clarifying for understanding

Practicing personal self-awareness

Paraphrasing and Summarizing

Practicing situational awareness

Elements of

Active Listening

Reflection techniques

Observing body language

Embracing empathetic presence

Practicing non-judgement

Giving full attention to the speaker

Listening for content and feeling

The Power of a Good Question

Thou shalt not celebrate without thine calendar's permission . . . Thou shalt not eat dessert before dinner...Thou shalt not jump in puddles . . . and other rules that don't exist. – **Penguins Can't Fly (and 39+ Other Rules that Don't Exist)**

Jason Kotecki writes and illustrates a fun romp fighting against "rules that don't exist." He explains life can be lived more fully and joyfully if, occasionally, you eat the chocolate cake you love first (before the salad) or consider breaking out the fancy china, even if it's just a Tuesday. How many such "rules" and other limitations do we each have?

> *We sat waiting for dinner, and though I cannot remember the context, I mentioned that I had an affinity for sunglasses; they just look cool, and if I had my way, I'd probably own "real" Aviators (in multiple colors), but "I have this really nice pair of Costas, a gift." Extravagant, silly, vain beyond further need for thought, I had long since concluded. He considered my state-ment, then looked at me speculatively and asked: "What is there to say you can't have more than one pair of nice sunglasses?" It may seem self-evident that owning two pairs of nice sunglasses is possible (even reasonable, a pair for the car and for jogging, let's say), but for some reason, this one line felt entirely earth-shattering. Certainly, there was extravagance and vanity to consider, but perhaps the vice of wanting Ray-Bans and Costas was forgivable, perhaps even a justifiable "treat yo'self" moment. My worldview suddenly expanded to include that I could own two pair of sunglasses. It has become a personal mantra to mean, "Why not? What is to say you can't?" Now, one of my favorite experiences is helping mentees cast off such self-imposed limita-tions: "What is there to say you can't do a PhD and a residency? Why not?"*

Sunglasses drawn by a mentor in a congratulations card.

The beauty of a good question is it invites both the asker and the asked on an adventure together to consider the answer. With artful subtly, it creates two-way dialogue. Questions hold singular power to both establish and deepen a relationship: gently influencing a conversation one direction or another, changing perspectives, infusing optimism, creating spaces for reflection, and offering new solutions. They clarify both individuals are on the same page as much as initiate new action.

A good mentor has an ability to both ask a thought-provoking question and then serve as the soundboard for the answer. In this way, a mentor avoids telling a mentee what to do and instead invites them along a journey of problem solving and action taking.

When asking questions, a mentor should be:

1. **Patient,** allowing the mentee time to marinate

2. **Prepared,** for any answer (to provide a judgement-free ground for further exploration)

3. **Present,** to fully listen to the answer (listening can be life-changing)

Increasing your conversational and questioning tools is well worth the effort. Books like *Conversational Intelligence* by Judith Glaser describe "listening to connect" and *10 Steps to Successful Mentoring* by Wendy Axelrod provides lists of questions to ask mentees. Moreover, increasing your toolbox of Thinking Tools (or how to think about thinking) is very helpful: Daniel Kahneman's *Thinking, Fast and Slow*, *Black Swan* by Nassim Nicholas Taleb, or Adam Grant's *Think Again* are all wonderful reads on the strengths and foibles of the human mind.

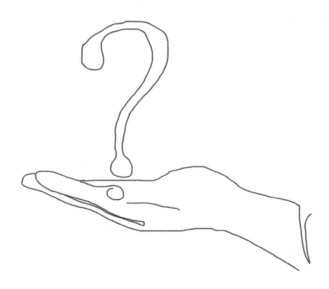

Personal Development Leads to Better Mentorship

Investing in your personal development is a means of investing in your mentees. This may seem counterintuitive: to say no to providing an opportunity for a mentee or reducing the total mentees you have to pursue further education, challenging new opportunities, or adopting some other personal practice. It can seem odd that increasing your self-knowledge may somehow help a mentee increase their own, but mentees benefit from these practices. Quite simply, it's pretty difficult to provide your experience on something you haven't actually experienced or help someone develop a skill you don't have yourself. Sharpening your skills as a mentor may include expressly developing classical mentorship skills:

- Attending workshops on mental health, mentorship, active listening techniques, and cultural awareness

- Taking personal inventories and assessments. Questionnaires exist for wellness, imposter syndrome, burn-out, emotional intelligence, leadership styles, personality types, and many more

- Reading articles and books relevant to your profession (e.g., best practices for precepting, efficiency strategies)

Personal development may also come in the form of seemingly unrelated pursuits because it may open the door for sponsorship opportunities or expanded worldviews that you can offer to mentees. Inspiration can also come from less career-oriented endeavors. I know that observing how a mentor of mine prioritized physical fitness, time in nature, and expanding horizons (I watched him get his first passport) as a means of becoming more his best self-inspired me to try things that stretched me that I had not before considered: weightlifting, traveling alone, reading "hard" books, etc.

Once, while struggling through a paper about Western blots (as part of a translational science project I accepted to "try something new"), a student asked what I was doing. I showed him the paper. His eyes lit up; "I had no idea a pharmacist could do that! I love pathophysiology!" This spurred him into taking electives in cellular mechanisms of disease and creating a new career path. He now knows far more than I on the topic of protein expression. He mentioned this once: "I don't know if this is really your passion, is it?" I agreed with him that cell signaling was not what woke me up in the morning, but helping someone else find their passion, now that did wake me up.

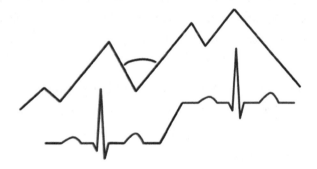

Mentorship Bookshelf

I never let my schooling interfere with my education. – **Mark Twain**

Mentorship is rarely part of the didactic curriculum and is often a tack-on portion of experiential training programs. A vast majority of training focuses on patient care, and would-be mentors are often left to their own devices to develop these skillsets. If you are interested in mentorship, pursuing workshops and continuing education on this topic is worthwhile. Additionally, a list of recommended reads (many of which are available in audio formats) is provided at the end of this book. Start creating your bookshelf today!

Know Thyself

Knowing others is intelligence; knowing yourself is true wisdom. – **Laozi**

To know thyself is the beginning of wisdom. – **Socrates**

When mentoring healthcare professionals, mentors can serve their mentees well by highlighting the importance of self-knowledge and self-reflection. These insights are integral to high-level teamwork requisite to healthcare delivery (as well as healthcare research and education). Self-knowledge can have far reaching implications into life as a whole.

Multiprofessional practice has been highlighted as the standard of care for patients, with key skills and traits necessary for optimal team performance, including adaptability, open communication, conflict resolution, cohesion, cooperation, coordination, and coaching between individual team members, among others.[29] The factors that go into effective team-forging are manifold (and include institutional culture), but at the foundation, a team is a group of individuals working together towards a common goal. Patrick Lencioni has proposed that in creating ideal teams, one also has to have ideal team players and identifies three key components for these individuals: humble, hungry, and (people) smart.[30] As mentors, we are helping to foster those ideal team players. Beyond the acquisition of clinical acumen, we are teaching people how to work within a diverse team.

Emotional intelligence is a cornerstone to teamwork. Defined as the "capacity to be aware of, control, and express one's emotions, and to handle interpersonal relationships judiciously and empathetically," Daniel Goleman's books repeatedly cite the relationship of emotional intelligence to both work success and personal happiness.[31,32] The foundation of emotional intelligence is *self-awareness* and *self-management,* which then lay the foundation for *social awareness* and *relationship management*. These four comprise emotional intelligence. How can mentors help their mentees increase their own self-awareness and self-management skillsets, which in turn facilitates emotional intelligence, which in turn fosters better team players (and maybe even promotes other important concepts, like diversity and wellness)? Personality inventories can be a fun, interactive, and approachable way to start conversations about self-insight, self-mastery, and ultimately, everyone's role on a multiprofessional care team. Helping people recognize strengths about themselves they hadn't realized before (as well as laugh at their own foibles) and spot new patterns in team dynamics can be highly rewarding. Commonly used inventories include Meyers-Briggs Type Inventory, DiSC°, and Clifton StrengthsFinder. All have associated books and websites worth investigating.

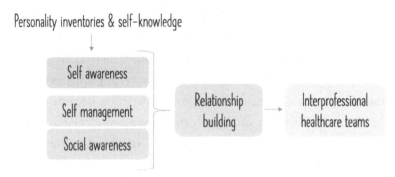

Personality inventories are far from perfect, including issues with test-retest reliability and lack of correlation to hard outcomes. As such, any test used should be taken with at least a few grains of salt. Even so, these tools may serve as an individual's first foray into stepping back from an interaction and evaluating their habits and patterns in the setting of others (or as Bruce Less says, "To know oneself is to study oneself in action with another person"). They can be a fun and light-hearted introduction to the heady and lifelong task of "knowing thyself."

These mentor-mentee discussions can offer a springboard for self-exploration and a common set of vocabulary among teams that can spark meaningful discussions for how each individual relates to themselves and the world around them.

The unexamined life is not worth living. – **Socrates**

Mentorship Promotes Diversity, Equity, and Inclusion

Over 50% of students today are first-generation college students. Moreover, there are still significant gaps of college attendance for racial and ethnic minorities, and these gaps are more pronounced at higher levels of achievement.[33] Similar disparities among genders are present in healthcare faculty roles as well. Although the solutions to appropriately addressing problems with diversity, equity, and inclusion are complex and require widespread change, mentorship may be part of this strategy.

Strategic leveraging of mentorship and advising programs has the **potential to increase access to mentors** and promote diversity. This has **positive benefits, not only on the individual,** but society at large. Evidence **suggests that anyone without a mentor** will have to put in extra work to **overcome gaps in knowledge, networks,** and experience. Because mentorship **has a compound effect over time,** with those being mentored accumulating **ever increasing social and professional** capital, the gap becomes more pronounced over time.

Actionable steps for individuals can be as small as attending workshops to enhance knowledge and awareness of key tenets within diversity, equity, and inclusion or including safe space verbiage on syllabi and profile pages. Taking time to learn skillsets about conducting open, culturally sensitive conversations will enhance the ability to connect, not only across cultures, but also likely within your immediate circles, as they often reinforce best practices of active listening and relationship management.

> *A few years back, I was talking with my old friends, and they asked me if I had ever considered the relative diversity of my mentees. I told them that usually mentees approached me based on interests in critical care or research. They pointed out some students may feel less empowered to do that, and I agreed to think on strategies to bridge that gap. A couple weeks later, I received an envelope in the mail with some stickers: the universal safe space sign, my pronouns,*

and a Ruth Bader Ginsburg dissent necklace (gifts from my friends).
I hung them in my office, feeling like it was a small step in the right
direction, but within a few months, I had multiple students come
to my office for advice, specifically citing that they liked my stickers.
It was a small act, but it resulted in some meaningful ripple effects.

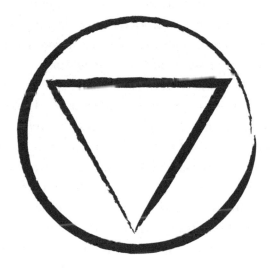

Notes on the Gender Divide

This story is about a series of coincidences that made me rethink the value of male-female mentorship dynamics, something I had not overtly considered previously. One morning, I was speaking with a male mentee, James, about a fellow pharmacist in our field. I mentioned that I admired his work and suggested he was someone to know. To my surprise, my normally happy-go-lucky mentee crinkled up his nose in near scorn and replied, "You fan girl about him, but you know he's only, like, two years ahead of you. I looked him up. I'm sure he's great, but you keep making it sound like I'm missing out by you being my mentor. I'm not." The passion and directness in James' voice stopped me in my tracks. Worried he had crossed some line, he retreated a bit and softly added, "I'll reach out to him, if you think it's a good idea, I'm happy to. Just don't sell yourself short." Later that day, a mentor of mine, also male, gave me feedback on a difficult e-mail I needed to write. A research project had gone south, and he was helping me navigate the next steps. His track changes shifted my first draft's tone entirely; it was still highly professional and polite, but it was now far firmer and more confident. The last line of his email stopped me in my tracks again: "Don't sell yourself short." Something interesting dawned on me that day; among my female colleagues, I was often praised for self-confidence (in fact, on StrengthsFinder, one of my top five is self-assurance) and had even been advised to tread more softly. Yet, here, twice in one day, I had been told by men I needed to believe in myself more and stand my ground. Both individuals knew me well, believed in me, and cared for me. The advice struck a chord. There are oft-repeated gender-based habits; women apologize more (and more often for things that aren't their fault, like "I'm sorry it's raining today") whereas men tend to view this practice as weakness. Men are more likely than women to apply for positions regardless of whether they have the qualifications on paper or not (and often actually get the job anyway), and they're more likely to ask for rais-

es and promotions (and receive them). The list goes on. Although gender studies and cultural gender-based socialization are complex topics, there appears to be a trend towards boldness among men, at least in the United States. Once I started looking for these scenarios, they struck me repeatedly. I was considering applying for a position. The two men I asked told me to "go for it, what can it hurt? Put your name in the hat," and the woman pointed out I technically wasn't qualified (I would end up getting the position). Another time, I mentioned how some statistical support would really change the game for my research project, my male colleague replied, "Have you asked your department chair?" When I did, I had an account opened the next day. When I thanked him for the idea, he replied bluntly, "You are still learning to manage up. You need to advocate for yourself more." Why had none of my female friends, all pharmacists, professionals, and strong women, given me this advice? I started to wonder if I needed to actively re-consider my own biases and try to be a bit more like my male counterparts. I began advising my mentees to apply for stuff (regardless of their official qualifications), to ask for the things they wanted and promote themselves, and to only apologize when it was truly warranted instead of as a filler phrase in conversation. It's hard to say the long-term effects, but when they tell me about new positions and experiences they got following this advice, it makes me think I'm onto something.

Mentorship, with its uneven power dynamics, introduces the possibility of mistreatment and harassment. This can feel especially clear in the setting of a male mentor/female mentee dynamic. While there must be no tolerance for sexual harassment and other types of discrimination, a male-female mentorship dynamic should not be avoided outright solely based on gender. Two high-profile, thoughtful commentaries have been published specifically on men mentoring women in the #MeToo era.[34,35] One noted that because women are under-represented in leadership positions, mentorship by current deans and other leaders for future female leaders likely *must* come from across the gender divide, and there may be specific benefits to a female having a male mentor.[12] Moreover, women leaders have specifically identified that male mentors were key to their success. Though it is too complex to say what gender-based differences result in specific benefits (e.g., a unique benefit of a female mentor to a male mentee), it is safe to say that everyone benefits from diversity in their mentorship teams and networks. This diversity ideally spans multiple domains: gender, race, age, socioeconomic class, profession, etc. Similar stories have been documented in other settings as well.[12] Finding a common ground in values and beliefs that are the foundation of mentorship gives us the ability to transcend the difficulties that may be present due to adding such diversity.

> *As a resident, I had several male preceptors with whom I developed great rapport. I'd walk onto the unit, and one would say a very hearty, "Good morning, Dr. Sikora!" which embarrassed me a little because pharmacists tend to use their first names, but I could tell it was in good humor. Oftentimes, this would be accompanied by a formal handshake, despite having known each other for over a year (and seeing each other daily). The others would follow suit, welcoming me into the circle, where we would joke a bit before getting serious about the day. Though not much of a sports aficionado, I became well acquainted with Tarheels basketball that year and enjoyed being "one of the guys" for a small part of the day. In them, I felt like I had a strong support group in case I ever needed anything, and to this day, they comprise a group of individuals that I know I can go to for advice. I think I practiced my handshake more times in that year than I have in my entire career combined, and every time I thrust out my hand to greet someone, I smile at this memory and even thank them in my head when I've received compliments for a confident handshake. Years later, I asked about this practice, saying it had meant a lot to me. "Ya know, guys slap each other on the shoulders and kind of kid around. It was like that. You were one of us."*

Creating a Mentorship Philosophy

Similar to a Teaching Philosophy, writing a Mentorship Philosophy provides a framework for how you will personally approach mentorship. This process fosters reflection on personal values and beliefs when it comes to mentorship and supports deliberate enactment of those values and beliefs in practice. All of this helps to form a mental model of mentorship.

Moreover, when initiating a mentorship relationship, taking time to understand the underlying philosophy of the mentor and the mentee can be a helpful activity to ensure that both individuals have appropriate expectations.

Considerations for a Mentorship Philosophy may include:

- Your conception of mentorship
- A description of your mentorship style and methods
- Justification for why this is your style and methodology
- Global goals for mentees
- Methods for assessment of yourself and your mentees
- What you perceive as the benefits of mentoring others versus what you hope mentees receive from you
- Your areas for professional growth
- What is your highest calling?

This can be summarized in answering four key questions:

1. Why I mentor
2. What I mentor about
3. How I mentor
4. How I measure my mentorship effectiveness

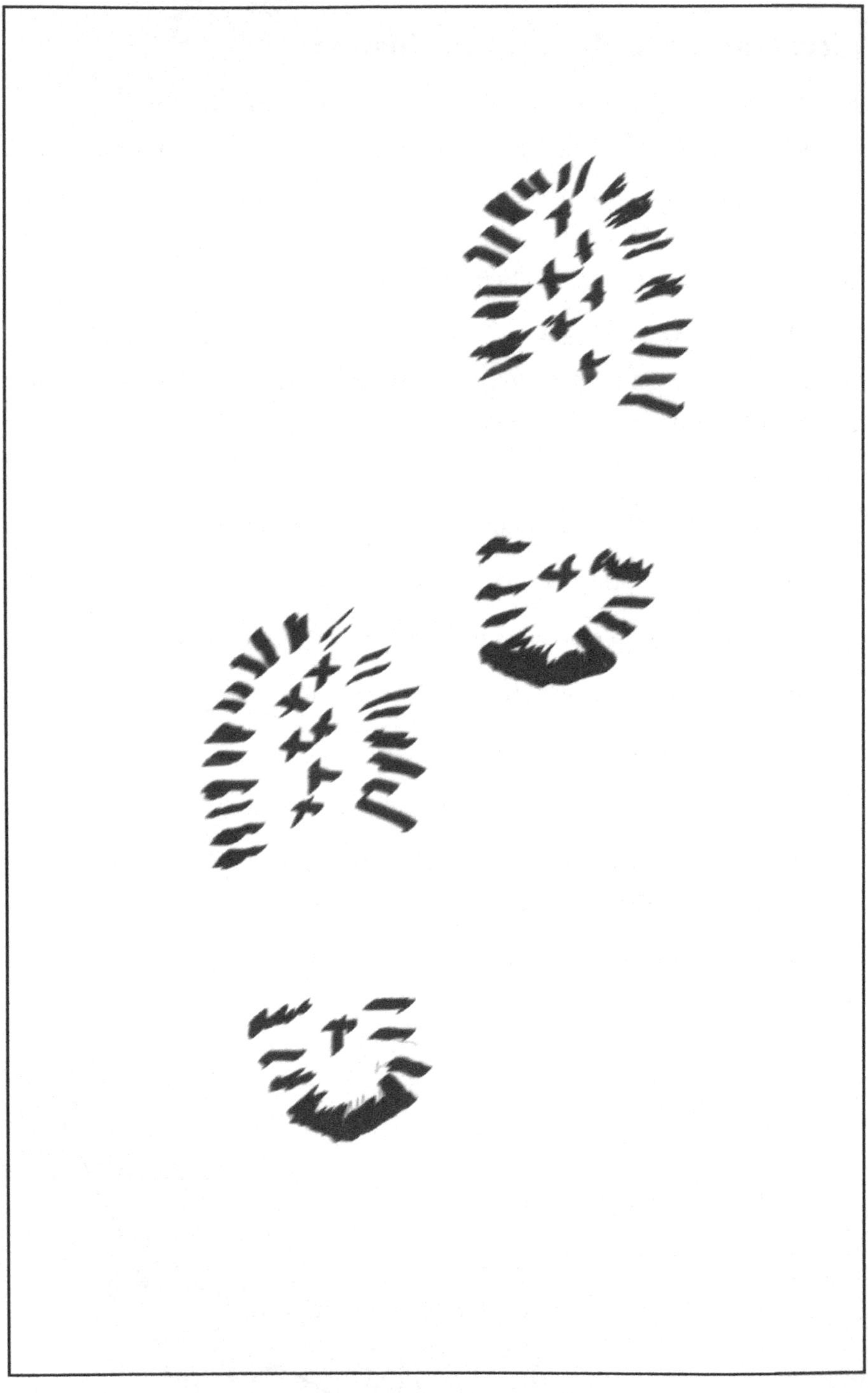

3

LOGISTICS

This section discusses different features of the mentorship journey and focus on how to make the most of the experience through good logistics and practical tips.

Evolution of the Roles in Professional Development

Mentoring relationships are dynamic. Driven by mutual growth, roles will transform over time as the needs, particularly of the mentee, change. For example, a student may connect with a professor in a mentorship capacity. The student may also select that professor to serve in an advising role for school-based activities. Herein, the mentor is also serving as a professor and advisor. Upon graduation, the mentor will now no longer be a professor or advisor but may then look for good opportunities for the new graduate as a sponsor thus evolving the relationship again. At some point, this relationship may even take the form of an entirely collegial or even friendship dynamic. These evolutions mature organically and likely underscore the importance of having multiple evolving relationships. The chemistry between two people should be valued, and these transformations may occur organically or through overt discussion.

Phases of Mentorship

1. **Initiation** is a trust building, goal-setting stage that is largely "task-centered."[36,37]

2. **Cultivation** is characterized by regular contact that transcends professional and personal domains and incorporates mutual growth. This stage is often highly fruitful from a productivity standpoint and is characterized by meaningful dialogue.[36,37]

3. **Separation** is marked by relationship disruption and even feelings of loss of trust, conflict, and resentment. As uncomfortable as this stage may be, it is a necessary for ultimate autonomous functioning of the mentee.[36,37]

4. **Transformation** marks the stage of viewing each other as colleagues, each with independent careers. Shared feelings of gratitude for the gifts of time spent together predominate this phase, although situation specific advice giving may still be present.[36,37]

Who Makes the First Move?

Traditionally, the onus of the first move is on the mentee. The thought process goes that this is the first hurdle that proves a mentee is a self-starter and driven in their career aspirations. Although this can be true, an alternative viewpoint is that some individuals may be less willing to make that first move due to feelings of imposter syndrome or not belonging (which may be especially true of first-generation college students and groups that are less privileged) or again, simple ignorance. If ignorance is not knowing what you don't know, a real possibility exists that talented, goal-oriented individuals just don't know what they're missing without a mentor. If an individual catches a potential mentor's eye for whatever reason (e.g., exemplary performance in the classroom, observed leadership traits, etc.), the potential mentor may feel empowered to reach out, stating interest in getting to know them or being available for questions.

A story. Or three.

(1) During my interview for my faculty position, I spoke with Allen, a scientist in our experimental therapeutics department. He excitedly told me about a new biomarker for respiratory failure, whose positive results had just come in. We had a lovely discussion, and when I wrote my traditional "thank you" emails following the interview, I posed an idea for him to consider that had popped into my head after the session had ended. Not viewing myself as a translational researcher, it was more of a question; "This is interesting to me. Have you thought about it?" Allen saw potential in this idea and reached out to me about using it as the basis of a KL2 grant application and offered to mentor me through my first grant proposal. Here was an opportunity both for a new mentor and an incredible learning experience that I didn't know I wanted (and indeed, didn't even know existed) without him making the first move.

(2) In a back-to-school event, students could drop their name in a hat and be randomly chosen to have lunch with us. I admit, I was put off by this more artificial construct, but Jo put her name in my hat, and we ate lunch together. The 90 minutes flew by as I got to know this student with whom I had never interacted before; she had impressive levels of involvement mixed with good humor, humility, and poise. I told her as much, gushing over her CV. I was curious about something though. At the beginning of the year, I tell the class that if they are interested in residency, please stop by (I have an open-door policy). Many take me up on the offer, but Jo hadn't. Towards the end, I said, "If I may ask, why did you put your name in my hat? Was this what you were looking for today?" Jo nodded emphatically and said, "Yes, even better," and seemed to sense my unspoken question. "I know you said that at the beginning of the year, but sometimes, those invites aren't really meant for everyone." She paused then, motioned to herself, as if calling my attention to her skin tone, different than my own. "And just because I wanted to do residency, didn't mean I was actually qualified. But this lunch thing you <u>had</u> to do, so it seemed like a good opportunity, though I didn't think I'd actually win it or that you'd reach out afterwards." "You're definitely qualified!" I replied, "And I admit that I thought the lunch thing was kinda hokey at first, but this has been a delight. One thing that would be nice for you to have on here is a research project, a publication. Have you done anything like that?" She said no, but she had an idea, and we got to work. Jo said she had no idea she was such a strong candidate, which blew my mind (if I was her, I'd be strutting around). A couple days later Jo had already implemented some edits I suggested for her CV and reached out to another pharmacist I thought she should talk to, the kind of follow-up you're hoping for from a mentee. What struck me about this scenario was someone who has all this potential, and yet, wasn't sure there was a space for them at the table, until "the mentor" made the first move.

(3) In my own journey, I was not always so pro-mentorship. When I was a resident, I had a defensive mindset; I didn't want preceptors to know that I didn't know something and did not want any cracks in the façade to show. One preceptor reached out to see if I might want to go with a group of them to this story-telling event and have dinner. The contestants competed for the best story, which could receive the Hippo Award. The thought of one more thing to do sounded exhausting. I said no. He invited me a couple more times. I said no then too. I was comfortable keeping the preceptors in my program at arm's length. He changed tactics; "I bought you a ticket. If you don't come, that's alright, but the ticket is yours if you want." He was in luck: I had no groceries at home, and the local food trucks sounded pretty good. The evening was surprisingly enjoyable and despite my standoffishness, I found myself talking about my frustrations with my research project, my dislike of this required seminar event, and feeling like I'd never get all of the cardiothoracic procedures straight. I can't say there was much life altering advice that came from that night, but it felt good to tell someone else who understood the medical (and institution specific) lingo. It felt good to laugh and be listened to. I hadn't known that I needed that evening as badly as I did, but the next morning, I walked into work with a fresh bounce in my step. Energized that someone cared enough to want to get to know me and to listen to the seeming banalities of my day-to-day, that I knew without a doubt there was an open door if I wanted to talk. It was empowering.

Getting Practical

Discuss Logistics and Define Expectations

Social norms for communication styles vary. Assumptions can lead to unfortunate misunderstandings. With four generations working together, discussion of professional use of social media, texting, and emailing is necessary. Interaction must be tailored to the practical and the comfortable for everyone. I've had mentors that I explore mountain trails with and also mentors where we formally meet for coffee at professional meetings. I've had mentees with whom we've investigated local hole-in-the-wall restaurants together and others where meetings only take place in my office.

I use a variety of communication channels with my mentees but always advise, "If you truly need me to do something for you, please email me and put the request in the title. Texting is for quick questions, updates, and fun." For meetings, I expect to be given drafts at least 24 hours prior to the meeting, so I can digest the material and appreciate when they come with specific updates and questions, but I also enjoy just catching up.

Key Elements to Relationship Structure

- Overall objectives, goals, and metrics for success
- What are we each looking for as an outcome to this relationship?
- Communication preferences in terms of medium, frequency, and timing (e.g., business hours versus evenings/weekends)
- Use of documentation (e.g., development plans, formalized feedback mechanisms)
- Meeting preferences. In-person via videoconference, ad hoc versus regular scheduled events, office-based or elsewhere
- Scope and boundary settings. Identifying if there are items within and outside of scope for this relationship is important. For example, there may be a setting where more personal discussions of family planning/work-life balance are topics of interest for a mentee. The mentor must decide if this is something they wish to explore and provide experience in
- The definition and limits of confidentiality
- Creating a process for regular touchpoints and feedback

Meetings and Deliverables

Schedule and structure of meetings is highly dependent on the context of the relationship and the needs of the mentee. Intensity and frequency may wax and wane over time.

For mentors, the bulk of the work is during the meetings, so it is important to prepare in advance and to bring your best self to the meeting. The guidance provided in the form of dialogue and questions is essential to the relationship. This is the time when you are helping align activities with goals and providing emotional support to enact the plans associated with those goals. However, for the mentee, the bulk of the work happens between meetings—field-testing behaviors, exploring new ideas, reflecting, etc. These efforts become the fodder for the dialogue during the meetings.

Meetings often benefit from having a past, present, and future structure to them: some catching up and/or debriefing, then discussing present thoughts, concerns, and ideas, and finally focusing on strategic planning. Homework between meetings will vary based on the situation (e.g., "why don't you research fellowships versus residencies, and we can talk more about that next time?"). It may also come in the form of joint work on deliverables. For me, I try to split meetings between "work sessions," where we are expressly focused on a work product (e.g., discussing the data analysis plan) versus "life chats," my catch-all term for mentorship meetings.

Some mentor-mentee relationships will be nearly entirely dialogue based with no joint deliverables. However, in healthcare, there are often many opportunities where mentoring is happening in conjunction with a deliverable (e.g., a grant proposal). In this case, it is important to remember that this work product has additional responsibilities beyond the psychosocial aspect of the relationship, so delineated responsibilities and roles, deadlines, meeting invites, emails with clearly stated requests, and open communication channels are essential.

Mentees are advised to be cognizant of project-related "digital body language," and mentors should guide their mentees on best practices depending on their level of expertise (for example, when I work with pharmacy students, this is likely one of their first professional projects, so I tell them explicitly the expectations: Outlook invites, Cloud-based share drives, timelines).

When working with early-career professionals, they tend to require less overt guidance, and I allow them autonomy to lead the process of finding a good mutual strategy. Mentees are further advised to realize that the quality of the product and level of communication surrounding that work-product are often viewed as direct indicators of their level of investment in the relationship. Take ownership of how assigned deliverables are integral to a mentor's career goals. They may have given you more responsibility than you realized without you specifically asking about the bigger picture.

Evaluate "Return on Investment" (ROI)

ROI for each deliverable must be carefully assessed.

- How does this product advance career goals?
- What new skills will the mentee learn?
- How will the mentee be awarded credit?

Wendy Axelrod[19] advises that deliverables meet criteria for the three "A's" – *ambitious, accountable,* and *advocated*. A fourth "A" is worth adding – *after-action reviewed.*

1. The scope of the project should be appropriately *ambitious*: a novel experience that stretches the mentee's skillset.

2. The project should be *accountable* in its ability to bring value to the mentee, the mentor, their network, and the profession.

3. The project should be *advocated* in that the mentor has the requisite time and experience (or can identify other content experts to provide this expertise) to ensure the project can be successfully completed.

4. The project should undergo an *after-action review* or a debrief.

Best Practice: Debrief or don't do it

From his years in the corporate world, my dad picked up "AARs" or "After Action Reviews." We 'AAR'ed everything from our trip to Paris (highlights, what we would do different) to poor performance on a test (how would you study next time?). It taught self-reflection but also was a time to share and connect. Activities shared between mentors and mentees should be discussed. If they weren't worth the time to debrief, they probably were not worth doing in the first place.

Mentee Pro-Tips

Mentoring is a brain to pick, an ear to listen, and a push in the right direction. – **John C. Crosby**

If you have found a good mentor, you can assume they want to help. Let's focus on helping them help you! Cognitive Load Theory says we have limited working memory capacity (and shy away from tasks with excessive demands). Streamlining cognitive load is important for everything from classroom learning to television commercials (the easier it is for someone to remember your brand, the more likely they are to buy it next time). A tip for exercising more is laying out your clothes the night beforehand; this simple act is a means of reducing cognitive load the next day and increases your chance of going for that jog. Reducing the cognitive load on your mentor is likely to increase engagement.

It is easier to edit than to create, and it is easier to react than generate. As such, providing first drafts of any working products and solutions to problems can help maximize what your mentor can offer. If you're asking for advice, don't just say, "What would you do?" but provide your potential solution to discuss.

- Make a point of expressing gratitude and providing updates to items discussed
- Inquire about logistics (e.g., calendar invites, communication preferences) that facilitate the relationship
- Mentees do well to find things to pick a mentor's brain about. Show up ready to talk openly. Be open to the push in the right direction.
  - "Can I pick your brain?"
  - "Can I get your take on something?"
  - "May I ask you a question?"

- Follow up on advice taken. This is feedback for the mentor and nurtures the relationship and allows the mentor to improve their style. It also creates future fodder for discussion

- Reflect, identify your "why," consider writing a personal mission or purpose statement

- See that your mentor is hoping to make an impact and take advantage

- Shop questions around to different mentors and consider conflicting advice with regard to personal strengths and resources

- Set goals and track progress in a way that fosters your own accountability (and engagement from your mentor)

- Stretch yourself, seek challenges, and be open to evaluation

- Understand the context of a project to a mentor's own career goals

The Power of Solitude

In *Lead Yourself First*[38], the power of solitude and reflection to foster clarity, creativity, emotional balance, and moral courage are discussed. Mentors can encourage such practices in their mentees (e.g., "schedule think time"). While the value of mentors asking challenging, open-ended questions is often discussed, mentors play a role in helping the mentee devise strategies to actually think through these questions. Scheduling time to explore current challenges and future directions yields higher quality dialogue.

> *When I was interviewing for a position at my alma mater, my last session was with Jeff, the Assistant Dean, with whom I had good rapport. We caught up about the last few years, and Jeff told me how excited he was to have me here. Then, he asked, "Where do you see yourself in 5 years?" I blanked, even stuttered, and finally said, "I am embarrassed I don't have an answer for one of the most classic interview questions there is, but you see, this is my 5-year plan. I realized during my 3rd year of pharmacy school, I wanted to work here, so I graduated, completed two years of residency, and have worked for the last year and a half as a clinician. I haven't thought any further than being in your office right now." Jeff laughed and said, "Well! Sounds like that is what you'll be doing in the first few months!"*

> *Later, I told Elizabeth about this moment (the one who first encouraged me to figure out a 5-year plan). She smiled, "The part no one realizes about this job is how much time you spend with the door closed, not "doing" anything. Thinking. Reading. Planning. Jeff is right; that is what you should be doing. You have to schedule the time too, or people will put meetings on your calendar and soon, you'll just be replying to emails, going to meetings, thinking you're productive because you're busy but not realizing there is no broader thought to it. It is the hallmark mistake of junior faculty not to spend time alone envisioning*

that strategy." In a world often marked by busy-ness, produc-
tivity metrics, and many pressures, being given permission
(and maybe an imperative) by two people I deeply respected
started me on my practice of "no meeting days" or walking the
block around the building: creating time to think.

The *"Busy" Trap*, an essay in the *New York Times* by Tim Krieder, is essential reading. From Bill Gates' famous "think weeks," where he unplugs for a week twice a year to read and reflect alone to the practice of journaling or even walking/jogging without music or audiobooks, finding time to let the mind process can have profound implications on the emotional processing needed to continue to care for patients day after day. It can also be a well-spring of creativity and insight. Rumi, Darwin, Thoreau, Emerson, and so many other great minds repeatedly sing the praises of silence and solitude. A recent book, *Every Deep-Drawn Breath*, the physician Dr. Wes Ely discusses his practice of early morning swims as a source of research insight. Encouraging mentees to create healthy solitude and reflection habits is all the more important in the era of hyper-digital connection. The research linking smartphones/social media to the breakdown of meaningful, in-person interactions and solitude leading to mental health issues like depression and anxiety is compelling enough to warrant conversation.[27]

Moral Courage

A career in healthcare will inevitably entail ethical dilemmas that range from the patient's bedside to the scholarly domains. Faced with difficult decisions, verbalizing values and having the moral courage to uphold these values are necessary. These types of quandaries can happen at any career stage. There are many sources of such courage, and mentors play a key role in helping talk through these scenarios.

"The source [of courage] might be one's bond with a friend or mentor…a relationship with a respected colleague…when clarity about the reasons for his actions is no longer enough to sustain a leader, he can seek out these sources. What he seeks, usually, is not still more clarity about the reasons for his actions, but simply reassurance: reassurance that what he is doing is right, that he is doing his best, that he is a good person notwithstanding what the critics say. To sustain moral courage, a leader must tend to the soul."[38]

Mentors are vital sources of this reassurance and act as checkpoints and gut checks along the way. Being able to go to someone who knows your backstory to gain perspective or reassurance can provide the mental fortitude and moral courage to make tough decisions in the face of conflict and adversity.

Creativity

In *Deep Work*[39], Cal Newport describes the two skills to thrive in the 21st century economy:

1. The ability to quickly master hard things

2. The ability to produce at an elite level

These abilities are summed in the concept of "deep work" or the "ability to focus without distraction on a cognitively demanding task" in order to create or develop a novel solution or product. His book is a highly compelling read that explains the essential nature of being able to prioritize deep work as a means of career success and satisfaction both. Healthcare delivery, research, and education requires creativity and problem-solving that deep work enables; achieving the mental state necessary for highly creative outputs requires a certain distraction-free zone (notably, the best study practices also include minimizing smartphone and other disruptions). Helping mentees re-frame their most important projects into the mindset of deep work principles is an important activity.

When I was writing my first grant proposal, I found that I could only work about 45 to 90 minutes before I fizzled out. I felt guilty about this inability to work longer but found the best strategy was to prioritize my morning session (my best and most creative time) for making some small progress before calling it quits. Then one day, a mentee came by to say goodbye and give me two gifts: a hand-painted canvas and a book, Deep Work, "for your bookshelf." In truth, my bookshelf is a source of pride for me because of gifts like hers. When I read Deep Work, I was amazed by how many of my struggles were validated. In attempting to learn grantsmanship, I had taken an aggressive stance on my calendar refusing meetings before 11am in order to focus (to the distaste of my co-workers). Moreover, I had struggled with feelings of guilt and even shame that I just couldn't make myself work any longer than an hour before I needed a break (preferably biking). How did I justify this? I work for an hour than go bike ride?! Deep Work explained it; for a novice, the most intense concentration they're capable of is an hour (an expert can get to four), the book says it's a good idea to block meetings and email-reply times to reduce distractions, and yes, exercising as a form of mental break was used by some of the greatest scientists. It was a catharsis for me, a truly great gift, and one that has transformed how I think about productivity and creativity. I love it all the more because it came from a mentee.

Providing Guidance

Mentors serve as guides. This guidance may take the forms of question-based exploration, advice giving/experience sharing, and feedback. The mentee owns both the decisions and the effort that is required to achieve their goals. Less prescriptive styles using open-ended, guiding questions may be optimal to achieving mentee buy-in.

Socratic Method: Defined as "a form of cooperative argumentative dialogue between individuals, based on asking and answering questions to stimulate critical thinking and to draw out ideas and underlying presuppositions," this style is highly characteristic of a mentor-mentee relationship: debate, dialogue, exploration, critique, and critical thinking.

Advice: At times, the relationship may be well established where more direct advice is appreciated without undermining a mentee's autonomy, e.g., during my first year in my faculty job, a long-time mentor said simply, "You should propose a continuing-education presentation for the state meeting in October." Because of our established history, I knew I wasn't being "told what to do" but trusted the no-frills, direct delivery was to imply, "This would be a very good idea, and you'll thank me later." Indeed, I thanked them later. Thoughtful sharing of experience can be useful here as well.

Giving Homework: At times, a mentee—no matter how talented or driven—simply does not know what they do not know. Mentors can provide overt direction (e.g., "For the next meeting, consider these questions" or "it may be worth doing some research on such and such before we talk again").

Feedback: Feedback should be solicited throughout the evolution of a mentoring relationship. However, beyond direct solicitation, a healthy relationship likely includes ad hoc feedback. I remember the day a distraught student came to my office. Nearly two hours later, they walked out much calmer. I felt exhausted and was unsure if I had managed it as well as I could have. Right then, my long-time mentor (and office neighbor) came to my door and said, "I didn't hear everything, but I could tell she was really upset. You handled that so artfully. I am so proud of you." It was feedback I really needed.

Reframing Feedback by Unlocking a Growth Mindset

We all need people who give us feedback.
That's how we improve. – **Bill Gates**

Mentorship is about growth, and growth is not always easy. In fact, growth can feel uncomfortable and even painful. Moreover, difficult feedback from a mentor (or telling them about recent negative feedback) can be tough because of the high value placed on their opinion. However, feedback and growth go hand-in-hand. Adam Grant sums it up beautifully: "Withholding feedback is choosing comfort over growth. Staying silent deprives people of the opportunity to learn. If you're worried about hurting their feelings, it's a sign that you haven't earned their trust. In healthy relationships, honesty is an expression of care." [6]

Though not a universal truth, many individuals that go into healthcare are used to being high achievers and less used to receiving difficult feedback. Helping mentees navigate this reframing process is a key role of a mentor.

View Feedback as a Gift

However, balance this gift with that not all feedback must be internalized or acted upon. Mentors can encourage mentees to check in with trusted people when difficult feedback comes.

Best Practices for Feedback

1. Be specific – Give examples and details

2. Be impactful – Frame how it fits into their goals

3. Be kind – Focus on actions (not character)

I am bound by my own definition of criticism: a disinterested endeavor to learn and propagate the best that is known and thought in the world. – **Matthew Arnold**

Difficult Conversations

*Profound thoughts arise only in debate, with a possibil-
ity of counterargument, only when there is a possibility
of expressing not only correct ideas but also dubious
ideas.* – **Andrei Dmitrievich Sakharov**

Seek to Be Challenged (not agreed with)

Difficult conversations are instrumental to growth. Crucial conversations have been defined as containing three key elements: opposing opinions, strong emotions, and high stakes.[40] Unsurprisingly, mentoring relationships in healthcare can result in such scenarios. Opposing opinions are inevitable and any time true connection is present, so too will be some level of emotion. Finally, the high stakes are present because patient care is involved as well as key career decisions. First and foremost, these conversations should not be avoided. As Kerry Patterson writes, "The mistake most of us make in our crucial conversations is we believe that we have to choose between telling the truth and keeping a friend."

The authors of *Crucial Conversations*[40] provide an excellent toolkit for conducting these conversations with key elements highlighting the power of dialogue (which cannot be understated for an effective mentor-mentee relationship in and of itself) and beginning the conversation by clearly starting with the heart and stating your path. By focusing on the motives behind what makes the conversation crucial (which includes feelings of genuine altruism and care for the other person) and refusing to see such a dialogue as a zero-sum game (but instead, a win-win situation where both individuals stand to learn something), mentors and mentees can navigate these moments.

The ability for both parties to understand the relevant information in an atmosphere characterized by both respect and care is vital. The ability to reflect on one's personal experiences and identify what factors have generated strong emotion are important. Such conversations include stating the path, sticking with facts, and an interest in empathetic listening and mutual testing of ideas.[40] Dean Rusk sagely said, "One of the best ways to persuade others is with your ears—by listening to them."

Difficult conversations are opportunities for exploring new paths and strengthening the relationship through trust building.

Inspiration for Seeking Feedback and Having Difficult Conversations

If you are irritated by every rub, how will you be polished? – **Rumi**

Our lives begin to end the day we become silent about things that matter.
—**Martin Luther King Jr.**

Constantly seek criticism. A well thought out critique of what you're doing is as valuable as gold. – **Elon Musk**

Find a group of people who challenge and inspire you, spend a lot of time with them, and it will change your life forever. – **Amy Poehler**

As iron sharpens iron, so one person sharpens another. – **Proverbs 27:17**

Cognitive Distortions

In Oliver Sack's, *The Man Who Mistook His Wife for a Hat*, Mr. Thompson suffers severe memory loss from Korsakov's syndrome. In the absence of a plausible story for why him and Dr. Sacks are conversing, he rapidly confabulates stories; he is a butcher cutting off "haifa pound of Virginia, a nice piece of Nova" or Dr. Sacks is his "old friend Tom Pitkins . . . me and Tom . . . was always going to the races together."[41]

Creating stories from available information is something we all do and even teach our trainees. With pharmacy trainees, we ask, "if you see vancomycin, cefepime, norepinephrine, fentanyl, and propofol ordered, what do you think?" (Answer: A septic patient undergoing mechanical ventilation). Nobel laureate Daniel Kahneman writes in *Thinking, Fast and Slow* about heuristics people use to make these sorts of rapid judgements. A heuristic is a cognitive shortcut or rule of thumb that can help simplify decisions, especially in conditions of uncertainty. However, while useful, these heuristics are highly prone to bias.[42] When these stories or heuristics go too far, they become cognitive distortions (a negatively biased automatic thought pattern). Without awareness, these distortions predispose individuals towards disconnection and even depression.[43] Spotting cognitive distortions (and asking thoughtful questions to help mentees re-evaluate) is a useful tool in a mentorship toolkit.

James would bop around the school, tossing his backpack and whitecoat on the lobby seat as if it were his living room couch. In the classroom, something about his exaggerated slouch and flashing smile made me certain that he was laughing at me. I was already a bit self-conscious in my role as a new teacher. I imagined a group text swapping jokes at my expense ("Is she really this excited about hemodynamics? How many times did she say, 'there's more than one way to skin a cat?'").

Protecting myself, I labeled him: entitled, smart aleck. Abruptly, it dawned me on this same student that slouched in his chair was the same one that repeatedly answered the toughest questions. James attended every class well-prepared. Sometimes, his answers were wrong, but he was right a lot too. It takes guts to be wrong in front of 140 classmates. I laughed at myself; I didn't know he was laughing at me. I had labeled, mind-read, and more. What kind of educator was I? I'm grateful I rethought these labels, as we ended up working together closely. Once you start looking for cognitive distortions, you can find them all around you. It can hone your thinking to think about your thinking.

Common Cognitive Distortions[43,44]	Example in the Training Setting	Assessment Questions
Blaming: Externalization of the source of negative feelings onto other individuals	Placing the preceptor's frustrations solely onto a (poorly performing) trainee	What is my role in this scenario?
Catastrophizing: Belief that events will be intolerable	Statements like "This trainee will kill someone" over relatively minor oversights that would be expected in the learning process	Am I assuming the worst?
All-or-Nothing Thinking: Viewing events in black-or-white or dichotomous categories	Statements like, "They'll never understand" when someone needs multiple explanations	Can I look for shades of gray?
Discounting Positives: Minimizing positive events that occur	Ignoring a trainee's successes or positive qualities	Is there another way to look at this situation that would enhance rather than compromise my emotional and mental wellbeing?
Labeling: Assigning negative traits/titles to oneself or others	Making broad generalizations about learners based on generational differences	Am I making this personal when it isn't?
Mind Reading: Believing you know another individual's thoughts without adequate evidence	They didn't do this note how I wanted it because they don't care	What evidence do I have to support this thought or belief?
Negative Filtering: Limiting focus to negative aspects	Fixation on perceived deficiencies in the trainee's skillset	Do I have a trusted friend whom I can check out these thoughts with?
Overgeneralizing: Extrapolating a pattern of negativity from isolated events	Seeing one missed deadline as a sign of poor project management	Am I overgeneralizing?
What If: Perpetual creation of 'what if' scenarios and dissatisfaction with answers	Creation of "what if" scenarios regarding negative evaluations from trainees	Is this thought helpful?

Signs of a Lagging Relationship

High-quality mentoring relationships are energizing and inspiring. If spending time with your mentor or mentee feels deflating or unvalued, this may be a sign that the relationship needs maintenance or that it has run its course. A few signs of a lagging relationship:

1. You don't feel energized after spending time together
2. The questions and conversations lack depth
3. Meetings end early and/or begin to feel repetitive in topics
4. Lack of progress updates or repeated failure to incorporate advice
5. Boundaries are not honored

Advice from a trusted mentor is a springboard for reflection, regardless of whether action is taken. A careful balance must be struck. A mentee needs to feel empowered to make their own decisions and to feel supported, yet if a mentee rarely heeds the advice provided, this is potentially the sign of a poor match.

There is no perfect formula for how much advice should be heeded, but patterns of inaction or lack of reflection must be evaluated. As Rocio Del Mar succinctly put it, "Even if your mentor is great and is giving you great advice if you're not intentional in applying the advice, you will not see any improvements."

One time an interviewer asked me, "What made you apply for this position?" In truth, the answer was, "Elizabeth told me to." She was someone who knew me very well and whose good ideas and advice repeatedly generated positive results for me. Given the strength of our relationship, I was comfortable that if she suggested something, it was worth my time to explore, without much further questioning. I answered with a conspiratorial smile, "My mentor said so." They laughed. I went on, "She said it was a good next step for me based on my goals of being a faculty member involved with clinical research. She said the program was new, so she didn't know too many specifics but that the experiences could be invaluable, so I am excited to find out more!" The interviewer said she sounded like a great mentor, and I said, "The best." I got the position, and it turns out she was absolutely right; it was invaluable. This was experience that I didn't know I needed. Even if she had been able to give me specifics and explain exactly how I'd someday use them, my own ignorance may have prevented me from realizing the sound advice I was being given. Thus, I took her advice on a blind leap of faith that she truly knew me and was giving advice worth heeding. I have had several relationships with this level of trust. As a product, my rule has been that if they give me advice, my bias is to act on that advice (even if I do not immediately agree or see the full rationale) based on my trust in them. If the advice didn't sit right with me, my respect for them was enough to spend time reflecting on my rationale and circling back to discuss, making it clear that I valued their input. These discussions were often very fruitful for learning more about each other and considering different perspectives.

No mentor's goal should be to create a "mini-me" or someone that blindly follows all advice, but ideally, there is enough trust and equity built up in the relationship that a good enough reason to try something new is simply, "my mentor told me it was a good idea." That being said, a mentor's goal is to help the mentee figure out things on their own, often things that have never been done before.

Signs of a Thriving Relationship

1. Presence of debate, differing opinions, and open dialogue
2. Prioritization of face time and time spent together
3. Productivity and creativity
4. Feeling energized from spending time together

Boundary Management

An unfortunate reality is that a good mentor may be one of the first or only people in someone's life where they feel heard and valued. It can be easy to see yourself (or someone you love) in the mentee and feel emotionally involved. This can create scenarios where professional boundaries are crossed. Wendy Axelrod states it well; "Becoming too intertwined in your relationship has some hidden deficits of overdependence and transference, leading to mentoring drama."

Keeping the relationship within a professional scope and within agreed upon boundaries is important to avoiding mentees becoming overly dependent (and even annoying in this process). It also helps the mentor to maintain no ego when it comes to a mentee's choices and providing caring, yet objective guidance. These scopes may be re-negotiated at various points, but mentors must guide mentees in this process. At times, mentor/mentee pairs will evolve into friendship, which has its own guiding principles and is a separate construct than mentorship. Thoughtful navigation of this process is necessary and can warrant specific conversations.

Increasing Influence

The interconnected, interprofessional healthcare system necessitates the ability to influence others. At the most fundamental level of healthcare is the clinician-patient relationship. From there, relationships branch to multiprofessional healthcare teams, research or advocacy teams, leadership, and education. A life in healthcare is a life about relationships. Thus, empowering mentees through the ability to gain influence to achieve outcomes through others is a key topic. Influencing others includes skills in relationship building, effective communication, and building credibility both at the local and professional level.

Learning how to speak up in meetings or promote oneself authentically are core to career advancement. Moreover, teaching mentees how to manage up gives them a toolkit that will be transferable to any job setting. In managing up, you manage your manager through various pro-active approaches (e.g., become a leader within the team, communicate priorities, seek feedback, anticipate the manager's needs, have insight into the manager's motivations and priorities, be a go-to source of help).

Fortunately, organizational psychology has furnished the relative layperson with tools that can be used to foster these skillsets. Even the nearing 100-year-old favorite, *How to Win Friends and Influence People* provides simple yet excellent advice.[45] (In fact, my personal joke is that many of the authors you see on the *New York Times* best-seller list simply took one of his 30 tips and expanded it with contemporary research methodology.) Some include "become genuinely interested in other people," "show respect for the other person's opinion," and "let the other person do a great deal of the talking." He highlights praising others hard work, showing gratitude, and extending grace over mistakes. All these skills start with self-awareness and self-management, the foundations of emotional intelligence.

A basic understanding of body language (and how it communicates a majority of the message over the specific word choice) is helpful. *The Like Switch*[46], written by a former FBI agent, is a fun and approachable read. He discusses "gravity defying gestures" as signs of openness and friendship. An example is the "eyebrow pop," where we raise our eyebrows in friendly greeting to others. A nearly universal sign of "I mean well," try it the next time you're about to order at a restaurant and watch for the unspoken reply (usually a more genuine smile and a reciprocal pop).[46]

> *I will never forget going to a busy restaurant after reading The Like Switch. The hostess had just gotten through with a rather clipped exchange with a couple upset about the wait. A bit harried, she immediately told me it was going to be over an hour and to give her a second to take my name. I raised my eyebrows and tried to give a friendly smile and replied congenially, "Take your time. You've got your hands full, don't you?" It was incredible to see her shift in body language. She looked up immediately, giving me full eye contact for the first time. I smiled again, raised my eyebrows, and she smiled back. Then, her eyes scanned around the room, and before 5 minutes had passed, my "hour wait" had me sitting at a high-top table that had been hiding off in the corner and sipping an iced cold beverage. It reminded me of a poem called Small Kindnesses by Danusha Laméris, where she highlights the beauty in small exchanges, small kindnesses. "We want to be handed our cup of coffee hot, and to say thank you to the person handing it. To smile at them and for them to smile back." I was about to thank her for the table when instead she thanked me for my patience.*

Digital Body Language

Amy Cuddy's discussion of power poses (e.g., shoulders squared and feet slightly apart) can increase a person's sense of confidence (and thus, that others view them more favorably). Other topics worth discussing include "digital body language" or the type of attitude conveyed via technology.[47] Explaining how mentees can show engagement and excitement via the appropriate use of exclamation points, quick response times, and closed-loop communication (e.g., "got it" to indicate something was received) are important workplace habits that aren't usually taught in classrooms. Such habits can build trust via technology-based relationships. Moreover, a working knowledge of generational differences can be helpful. Certain practices like use of ellipses (I was thinking… we might consider…), emoticons (e.g., :), :p), and certain abbreviations (e.g., "brb" for "be right back") are associated with older generations that came to such technology before smartphone keyboards (i.e., T9 texting) compared to a nearly fluent use of emojis (and less abbreviations) by younger generations.[48] Understanding such generational differences can avoid unfortunate communication mishaps.

Efficiency Strategies

It doesn't matter what your system is so long as it works for you, but you have to have a̲ system. – **Jon Sikora**

For a productivity strategy to work, it must be personalized to the individual. Mentors can discuss their specific strategies and encourage mentees to do the same.

1. **Create an organizational system.** Robust to-do list apps, customizable physical agendas, and virtual calendars mean many tools are available.

2. **Avoid being the rate the limiting step**. Healthcare careers are a juggling act, so getting the ball in someone else's court and working on other things is vital.

3. **Overcome initial inertia**. Sometimes projects can feel overwhelming but setting aside 15 minutes to create a folder on the computer, save the Word document with the correct title, or download the appropriate background materials can get the ball rolling (and lets your mind problem solve sub-consciously).

4. **Treat yourself like your own best employee.** Avoid negative self-talk and saying, "I should be able to make myself do this." Figure out strategies that make the work fun and enjoyable. I treat myself to snacking on blueberries as motivation (and reward myself with Reese's cups).

5. **Break down to-do list tasks into small chunks that can be checked off.** Do not put "write manuscript." Instead, put "complete title page" and "update references."

6. *Eat That Frog!* **by Brian Tracy is a great introductory read to improving productivity**. Based on the Mark Twain quote, "Eat a live frog first thing in the morning and nothing worse can happen today." He advises identifying the frog that you need to

eat (i.e., the most important task of the day) and doing that first. He outlines 22 strategies, including *Planning Ahead, Preparing Beforehand*, and *Taking One Step at Time* to deliberately improve productivity. He concludes, "your ability to select your most important task at each moment, and then to get started on that task and to get it done both quickly and well, will probably have more of an impact on your success than any other quality or skill you can develop."

4

AN ONGOING JOURNEY

Mentorship is a lifelong journey.
A focus on wellness and promoting sustainability
of a healthcare career are essential.

| MAXIM | Metrics matter (but remember it's nature over number in a healthcare journey). |

Preventing Burn-Out

Burn-out is an increasing problem in healthcare, with COVID-19 fanning the flames. Burn-out is a syndrome conceptualized as resulting from chronic workplace stress that has not been successfully managed. It is characterized by three dimensions: feelings of energy depletion or exhaustion; increased mental distance from one's job, or feelings of negativism or cynicism related to one's job; and reduced professional efficacy. [49]

The ramifications of burn-out for the individual include reduced wellness, poor sleep quality, poor physical health, depression, and suicide.[50,51] The ramifications on the healthcare system and patient safety cannot be undersold either, as burn-out can lead to high turnover rates, absenteeism, and leaving healthcare entirely. From the patient perspective, adverse effects from burn-out include medical errors, reduced quality of care, and lower patient satisfaction.[52,53]

Healthcare is a profession defined by caring for other people. Helping mentees identify and implement strategies against burn-out has become an essential aspect of modern-day healthcare mentoring. To care for others, you must first care for yourself. Mentors are encouraged to make a practice of openly discussing (and modeling) wellness for their mentees.

Discussing mental health, sleep, exercise, and nutrition patterns, taking time off work, and prioritizing hobbies are essential, not only for being an excellent provider of patient care and but also a healthy, fulfilled individual. Supporting mentees to mindfully concentrate on the present, be active agents regarding how they spend their most precious resources of attention, time, and energy, and prioritize living into personal values are vital parts of the mentorship process.

Promoting Wellness

Wellness is defined as "a holistic integration of physical, mental, and spiritual well-being, fueling the body, engaging the mind, and nurturing the spirit."[54] Beyond good health, it encompasses living life fully (thriving rather than surviving) and is a "lifestyle and a personalized approach to living life in a way that . . . allows you to become the best kind of person that your potential, circumstances, and fate will allow."

This approach means taking deliberate time and effort to evaluate your life and make thoughtful decisions and actions towards improving the overall quality of your lived experience. [55]

Wellness is a success metric mentors should encourage mentees to strive towards. Arianna Huffington writes in *Thrive,* "to live the lives we truly want and deserve, and not just the lives we settle for, we need a Third Metric, a third measure of success that goes beyond the two metrics of money and power, and consists of four pillars: well-being, wisdom, wonder, and giving." [56]

Termed "Sharpen the Saw" in Stephen Covey's *7 Habits of Highly Effective People*[57], caring for yourself requires deliberate planning and action: "Sharpen the Saw means preserving and enhancing the greatest asset you have–you. It means having a balanced program for self-renewal . . . we must never become too busy sawing to take time to sharpen the saw."

Wellness has eight key dimensions: intellectual, emotional, social, spiritual, vocational, financial, environmental, and physical. While no dimension can be entirely neglected, you will strategize differently to find an authentic, personal harmony among them.

If I had six hours to chop down a tree, I'd spend the first four hours sharpening the axe. – **Abraham Lincoln**

Dimensions of Wellness

Dimension	Habits
Intellectual	✿ Learning an instrument or other skilled craft ✿ Reading, taking classes, listening to podcasts ✿ Pursuing diverse experiences through travel or other cultural outlets (e.g., museums)
Emotional	✿ Practicing mindfulness: walking, journaling ✿ Pursuing counseling as needed
Social	✿ Attending social functions related to a spiritual community or hobby ✿ Pursuing high-quality interactions (e.g., in person meetings) over more shallow interactions (e.g., social media)
Spiritual	✿ Attending regular religious services ✿ Creating a daily devotional routine, which may include reading, meditation, etc.
Vocational	✿ Pursuing higher education or other certifications ✿ Taking on new challenges or commitments, especially in leadership or teaching roles ✿ Expanding one's comfort zone
Financial	✿ Creating an emergency fund that is at least one month's living expenses ✿ Working to eliminate debts ✿ Attending financial literacy workshops
Environmental	✿ Recycling and/or composting when possible ✿ Looking for means to reduce plastic wastes ✿ Considering charitable donations to organizations that protect the environment ✿ Exploring new habits that can improve one's carbon footprint or waste practices (e.g., re-usable plastic bags)
Physical	✿ Exercising regularly (including strength training) ✿ Sleeping 7 to 8 hours per night ✿ Eating a balanced diet ✿ Scheduling health appointments

Define your Success

Each individual's concept of success is unique. Taking time to deliberately define your personal metrics of success (and not subconsciously internalizing societal metrics) helps you to recognize milestones worthy of celebration as well as when you have strayed from your compass. Within this success, define your personal bar for excellence.

A career in healthcare is prone to feeling like you are caught in the rat race. Taking time to define your metrics of success (as part of a personal mission statement or otherwise) is time well spent. Two framed quotes hang from my office walls by Ralph Waldo Emerson and Max Ehrmann (this one given to me by a mentor no less!). They ground me to my essential values: humility, loyalty, passion, kindness, courage, equilibrium, excellence, honesty, gratitude, and integrity.

> *"What is success? To laugh often and much; to win the respect of intelligent people and the affection of children; to earn the appreciation of honest critics and endure the betrayal of false friends; to appreciate the beauty; to find the best in others; to leave the world a bit better, whether by a healthy child, a garden patch or a redeemed social condition; to know even one life has breathed easier because you have lived. This is to have succeeded!"*
> **– Ralph Waldo Emerson**

Desiderata of Happiness

GO PLACIDLY amid the noise and the haste and remember what peace there may be in silence. As far as possible, without surrender, be on good terms with all persons. Speak your truth quietly and clearly; and listen to others, even to the dull and the ignorant; they too have their story. Avoid loud and aggressive persons; they are vexatious to the spirit.

If you compare yourself with others, you may become vain or bitter, for always there will be greater and lesser persons than yourself. Enjoy your achievements as well as your plans. Keep interested in your own career, however humble; it is a real possession in the changing fortunes of time. Exercise caution in your business affairs, for the world is full of trickery. But let this not blind you to what virtue there is; many persons strive for high ideals, and everywhere life is full of heroism.

Be yourself. Especially do not feign affection. Neither be cynical about love; for in the face of all aridity and disenchantment, it is as perennial as the grass. Take kindly the counsel of the years, gracefully surrendering the things of youth. Nurture strength of spirit to shield you in sudden misfortune. But do not distress yourself with dark imaginings. Many fears are born of fatigue and loneliness.

Beyond a wholesome discipline, be gentle with yourself. You are a child of the universe no less than the trees and the stars; you have a right to be here. And whether or not it is clear to you, no doubt the universe is unfolding as it should. Therefore, be at peace with God, whatever you conceive Him to be. And whatever your labors and aspirations, in the noisy confusion of life, keep peace in your soul. With all its sham, drudgery and broken dreams, it is still a beautiful world. Be cheerful. Strive to be happy.

– **Max Ehrmann**

| MAXIM | Set your own bar for excellence. |

Identifying What Is Essential

Less but better. – **Greg McKeown**

Mentors can help mentees become essentialists. In Greg McKeown's expertly written book *Essentialism: The Disciplined Pursuit of Less,* he discusses "constantly defining where you can create the most value, then finding ways to execute it most effortlessly." He encourages:

1. **Exploring** (to identify the *few* items that are *essential*)

2. **Eliminating** (removing what is unnecessary)

3. **Executing** (reducing the amount of effort needed to achieve the identified priorities)

The transition from "I have to do all these things" to "I *choose* to do these few things that really matter" is important. Moreover, saying yes without thinking through the ramifications can lead to being overwhelmed with obligations. Discussing how to thoughtfully consider "what is essential" and reflecting on how to say yes more judiciously helps career sustainability. Taking active steps to avoid feeling out of control and overworked, and instead, experiencing joy in the healthcare career journey are extremely important for mentee wellbeing and success.

You see how few things you have to do to live a satisfying and reverent life? – **Marcus Aurelius**

Learning to Say No and Standing Your Ground

I sat in my mentor's office chitchatting about the week with no particular purpose beyond catching up. I mentioned I was busy and also that I had a newsletter due soon. Her face scrunched up like she'd smelled something bad, and she leveled me with a kind but firm gaze: "You never need to do another newsletter." In surprise, I replied, "Weren't you the one that <u>told</u> me to do newsletters?" "Yes, years ago. You've published enough and have a lot of higher yield activities to do now. Maybe you do one a year to maintain involvement with a group close to your heart or to create an opportunity for a student, but you really don't need to be doing those anymore."

This story captures so much of mentorship: (1) **A mentee doesn't know what they don't know.** I didn't know I should be graduating beyond newsletters until the moment she said so. (2) **The importance of face-time.** The only reason I brought it up is because she asked me how my day was, and I knew she genuinely wanted to know. (3) **Helping mentees prioritize activities.** In one comment, she changed my entire outlook to evaluate how I was spending my time. She was guiding me in the concept I've termed *sustainable excellence.*

| MAXIM | Sharpen the saw and define your non-negotiables. |

Sustainable Excellence

In recent years, healthcare workers have suffered from worsening mental health and increasing burn-out and attrition from the field. Burn-out is a multi-factorial problem that requires systematic change, but mentors must help their mentees to develop careers characterized by *sustainable excellence.*

Mentors must realize that "do as I say, not as I do" is unlikely to be effective because they serve as role models. Encouraging mentees to focus on mental health and wellness (e.g., good sleep, exercise) and managing their career as a marathon and not a sprint are vital responsibilities in the modern era. In particular, thoughtful discussion of a mentee's present responsibilities in terms of return on investment for their career and how it fits into their current life are vital discussions.

Mentees are frequently overwhelmed by good opportunities. Mentors are encouraged to help clarify, "Does this activity align with a sustainable pursuit of excellence?" In an engaged healthcare career, the number of "good opportunities" is staggering. Furthermore, there is always "more" that can be done to improve patient care, education of trainees, and personal knowledge and skill.

One of the core responsibilities of a mentor is guiding mentees to select which "good opportunities" most align with future goals and personal interests and moreover, to help start the process of identifying what is enough. Clarifying what opportunities directly relate to needed skillsets and experiences for future goals is an important conversation.

The graph shown is adapted from Murray et al. and displays the key concept reminiscent of the classic Frank-Starling curve that excellence falls along a sigmoid curve of individual; however, only one section of this graph has a 'sustainable' area of excellence. This is the zone mentors should help mentees strive towards.[59]

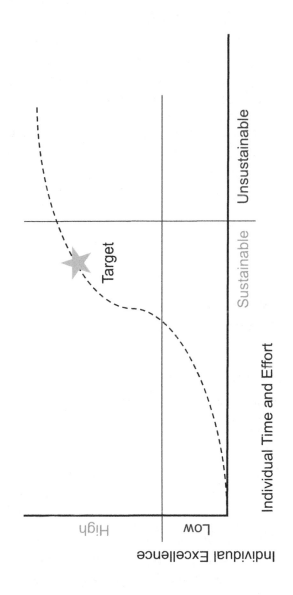

Auditing as a Form of Living Deliberately

I went to the woods because I wished to live deliberately, to front only the essential facts of life, and see if I could not learn what it had to teach, and not, when I came to die, discover that I had not lived. I did not wish to live what was not life, living is so dear. – **Henry David Thoreau**

Mentors can encourage mentees to think deliberately through guiding audits. Audits will differ by the individual and circumstance but aim to answer key questions.

1. How satisfied am I with this area of my life?
2. What has felt the most meaningful (and what doesn't)?
3. What is and is not going well?
4. What brings me the most joy?
5. How am I spending a majority of my time and energy (and do I like these investments)?
6. What are the greatest stressors? Are they modifiable?
7. What am I most proud of?
8. What types of thoughts/emotions are going in my head?

An example audit:

1. When thinking on how to live in a more deliberate fashion that increases wellness, consider one's core values. Review the list provided and select 3 to 5 values that are the most important to you. These central values can guide future decision making.
2. Reflect on one's core priorities in life. What are the dimensions that bring the most personal engagement and fulfillment? What are the areas of life that you wish you had more time or energy to focus upon? Examples may include family, friends, or hobbies.

3. Within the 8 dimensions of wellness, consider practices you already engage in that maintain wellness. Then, consider if this dimension may need more priority and what types of activities or practices are readily achievable in the near future to begin (e.g., a 30-day hiatus from social media sites or making a commitment to walk twice a week during a lunch break). Be thoughtful not to overextend yourself and consider creating a wish list as well as a readily implementable list that can be started soon.

4. Non-negotiables are a term to help prioritize core needs. These are activities or practices that are not negotiable to you and that you feel a personal commitment to fulfill at a high completion rate (i.e., "no matter what, I am going to..."). Examples include sleeping at least 7 hours a night or exercising three times a week. These are activities that, even when life gets very busy, will remain prioritized because of their essential role in maintaining your personal wellness.

5. Taking the time to define one's personal success or one's way of saying you lived the day well by your own standards can be a refreshing way to evaluate the day and the activities in it. Termed accountability questions, these questions function to clarify priorities, track progress, and also, create reasonable measures of success. These questions should relate to one's values and one's priorities.

Examples of accountability questions may include:

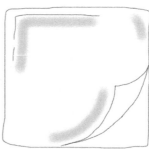

1. Did I learn something new today?

2. Did I help someone today?

3. Did I progress (in any fashion or degree) a long-term project?

Values List

Authenticity	Faith	Mindfulness
Acceptance	Fame	Meaningful Work
Achievement	Friendship	Openness
Adventure	Fun	Optimism
Authority	Gratitude	Peace
Autonomy	Growth	Pleasure
Awareness	Happiness	Recognition
Balance	Honesty	Reputation
Beauty	Humor	Respect
Boldness	Humility	Responsibility
Compassion	Influence	Security
Challenge	Joy	Self-Respect
Citizenship	Justice	Service
Community	Kindness	Spirituality
Competency	Knowledge	Stability
Contribution	Laughter	Success
Creativity	Leadership	Status
Curiosity	Learning	Truth
Determination	Love	Trustworthiness
Fairness	Loyalty	Wisdom

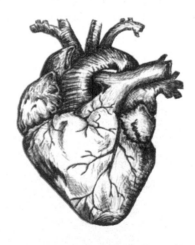

Pay It Forward

Learning to pay it forward can add a tremendous sense of meaning and dignity to our lives. – **Greg Epstein**

Mentorship is a multiplier. Framing your time and effort invested into a mentee as a means of making more mentors and viewing yourself as a multiplier of positive change is at the heart of mentorship.

The success of a mentor is measured not in how many students they have trained, but in how many mentors they have created. [58]

Mentorship has a powerful domino effect, and each of us is bestowed with the power to break negative cycles and create positive ripples in the generations to come. Mentorship is fundamental to our common calling of caring for others.

Growth is a never-ending process, and no matter what stage of career you are in, you have something worthy to share with someone and someone has something worthy to share with you. As John Wooden so beautifully said, "You can't live a perfect day without doing something for someone who will never be able to repay you."

True, you will never be able to pay back such a gift, but you can start today paying it forward.

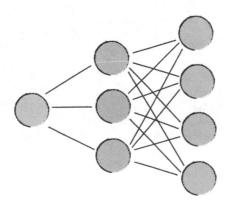

Hand-drawn gift from a former resident

REFERENCES

1. Benson SG, Dundis SP. Understanding and motivating health care employees: integrating Maslow's hierarchy of needs, training and technology. *J Nurs Manag.* Sep 2003;11(5):315-20. doi:10.1046/j.1365-2834.2003.00409.x

2. Linklater R, Thomas J, McLaren M, Schlosser E, Kinnear G, Copyright Collection (Library of Congress). Fast food nation. United States: Fox Searchlight Pictures; 2006. p. 12 film reels of 12 on 6 (ca. 116 min., ca. 10,440 ft.).

3. "Workplace Loyalties Change, but the Value of Mentoring Doesn't." Knowledge@ Wharton. The Wharton School, University of Pennsylvania, 16 May, 2007. Web. 06 January, 2022 https://knowledge.wharton.upenn.edu/article/workplace-loyalties-change-but-the-value-of-mentoring-doesnt/.

4. Kammeyer-Mueller JJ, TA. A quantitative review of mentoring research: Test of a model. *Journal of Vocational Behavior.* 2008;72:269-83.

5. Smart BJ, Haring RS, Zogg CK, et al. A Faculty-Student Mentoring Program to Enhance Collaboration in Public Health Research in Surgery. *JAMA Surg.* Mar 1 2017;152(3):306-308. doi:10.1001/jamasurg.2016.4629

6. Perumalswami CR, Takenoshita S, Tanabe A, et al. Workplace resources, mentorship, and burnout in early career physician-scientists: a cross sectional study in Japan. *BMC Med Educ.* Jun 3 2020;20(1):178. doi:10.1186/s12909-020-02072-x

7. Jordan J, Watcha D, Cassella C, Kaji AH, Trivedi S. Impact of a Mentorship Program on Medical Student Burnout. *AEM Educ Train.* Jul 2019;3(3):218-225. doi:10.1002/aet2.10354

8. Voytko ML, Barrett N, Courtney-Smith D, et al. Positive Value of a Women's Junior Faculty Mentoring Program: A Mentor-Mentee Analysis. *J Womens Health (Larchmt).* Aug 2018;27(8):1045-1053. doi:10.1089/jwh.2017.6661

9. Walensky RP, Kim Y, Chang Y, et al. The impact of active mentorship: results from a survey of faculty in the Department of Medicine at Massachusetts General Hospital. *BMC Med Educ.* May 11 2018;18(1):108. doi:10.1186/s12909-018-1191-5

10. Farkas AH, Bonifacino E, Turner R, Tilstra SA, Corbelli JA. Mentorship of Women in Academic Medicine: a Systematic Review. *J Gen Intern Med.* Jul 2019;34(7):1322-1329. doi:10.1007/s11606-019-04955-2

11. Grant AM. *Give and take : a revolutionary approach to success.* Viking; 2013:305 p.

12. Ensher EA, Murphy SE. *Power mentoring : how successful mentors and protégés get the most out of their relationships.* 1st ed. Jossey-Bass; 2005:vi, 355 p.

13. Daloz LA. *Mentor : guiding the journey of adult learners.* Second edition with new foreword, preface, and afterword. ed. The Jossey-Bass higher and adult education series. Jossey-Bass; 2012.

14. Dickson KS, Glass JE, Barnett ML, Graham AK, Powell BJ, Stadnick NA. Value of peer mentoring for early career professional, research, and personal development: a case study of implementation scientists. *J Clin Transl Sci.* Apr 8 2021;5(1):e112. doi:10.1017/cts.2021.776

15. Pinelli NR, Eckel SF, Vu MB, Weinberger M, Roth MT. The layered learning practice model: Lessons learned from implementation. *Am J Health Syst Pharm.* Dec 15 2016;73(24):2077-2082. doi:10.2146/ajhp160163

16. Conroy P, Minor W. *My reading life.* 1st ed. Nan A. Talese/Doubleday; 2010:x, 337 p.

17. Jones S LW, Murray B, Sikora A. Team science, layered learning, and mentorship networks: the trifecta for maximizing scholastic achievement for clinical pharmacists. *Am J Health Syst Pharm.* 2022;[In press].

18. Kleinpell R, Grabenkort WR, Boyle WA, 3rd, Vines DL, Olsen KM. The Society of Critical Care Medicine at 50 Years: Interprofessional Practice in Critical Care: Looking Back and Forging Ahead. *Crit Care Med.* Aug 16 2021;doi:10.1097/CCM.0000000000005276

19. Axelrod W. *10 steps to successful mentoring.* 10 steps. ATD Press; 2019:pages cm.

20. Dweck CS. *Mindset : the new psychology of success.* Ballantine Books trade pbk. ed. Ballantine Books; 2008:x, 277 p.

21. Ramani S, Konings K, Mann KV, van der Vleuten C. Uncovering the unknown: A grounded theory study exploring the impact of self-awareness on the culture of feedback in residency education. *Med Teach.* Oct 2017;39(10):1065-1073. doi:10.1080/0142159X.2017.1353071

22. Sinek S. *The infinite game.* 1st Edition. ed. Portfolio/Penguin,; 2019:1 online resource.

23. Newsome AS. Pay it forward. *Am J Health Syst Pharm.* Jul 7 2020;77(14):1166-1168. doi:10.1093/ajhp/zxaa125

24. Newsome AS, Ku PM, Murray B, et al. Kindling the fire: The power of mentorship. *Am J Health Syst Pharm.* Dec 9 2021;78(24):2271-2276. doi:10.1093/ajhp/zxab295

25. Charles F. *The thin book of trust*. Thin Book Publishing; 2nd edition.

26. Huffington AS. *Thrive : the third metric to redefining success and creating a life of well-being, wisdom, and wonder*. First paperback edition. ed. Harmony Books; 2015:xxiii, 342 pages.

27. Newport C. *Digital minimalism : choosing a focused life in a noisy world*. Portfolio/Penguin; 2019:xviii, 284 pages.

28. Peterson JB, Doidge N, Van Sciver E. *12 rules for life : an antidote to chaos*. Random House Canada; 2018:xxxv, 409 pages.

29. Kleinpell R, Grabenkort WR, Boyle WA, 3rd, Vines DL, Olsen KM. The Society of Critical Care Medicine at 50 Years: Interprofessional Practice in Critical Care: Looking Back and Forging Ahead. *Crit Care Med*. Dec 1 2021;49(12):2017-2032. doi:10.1097/CCM.0000000000005276

30. Lencioni P. *The ideal team player : how to recognize and cultivate the three essential virtues : a leadership fable*. Jossey-Bass, a Wiley Brand; 2016:xi, 219 pages.

31. Goleman D. *Emotional intelligence*. 10th anniversary trade pbk. ed. Bantam Books; 2005:xxiv, 358 p.

32. Goleman D, Boyatzis RE, McKee A. *Primal leadership : realizing the power of emotional intelligence*. Harvard Business School Press; 2002:xvii, 306 p.

33. Collective E. Pride and Pressure: What It Means to Be A First-Generation College Student. Accessed 1/6/22, https://emersoncollective.com/articles/2017/06/pride-and-pressure-what-it-means-to-be-a-first-generation-college-student/

34. Soklaridis S, Zahn C, Kuper A, Gillis D, Taylor VH, Whitehead C. Men's Fear of Mentoring in the #MeToo Era - What's at Stake for Academic Medicine? *N Engl J Med*. Dec 6 2018;379(23):2270-2274. doi:10.1056/NEJMms1805743

35. Byerley JS. Mentoring in the Era of #MeToo. *JAMA*. Mar 27 2018;319(12):1199-1200. doi:10.1001/jama.2018.2128

36. S H. The mentor¬protege relationship. *Am J Pharm Educ*. 2003;67(3):82.

37. K K. Phases of the mentoring relationship. *Acad Manage J*. 1983;26:608-625. doi:https://doi.org/10.5465/255910

38. Kethledge RM, Erwin MS. *Lead yourself first : inspiring leadership through solitude*. Bloomsbury USA; 2017:xxi, 214 pages.

39. Newport C. *Deep work : rules for focused success in a distracted world*. First Edition. ed. Grand Central Publishing; 2016:295 pages.

40. Patterson K. *Crucial conversations : tools for talking when stakes are high*. 2nd ed. McGraw-Hill; 2012:xviii, 244 p.

41. Sacks O. *The man who mistook his wife for a hat and other clinical tales.* Summit Books; 1985:xvi, 233 p.

42. Kahneman D. *Thinking, fast and slow.* 1st pbk. ed. Farrar, Straus and Giroux; 2013:499 p.

43. Leahy RL, Holland SJ, McGinn LK. *Treatment plans and interventions for depression and anxiety disorders.* 2nd ed. Treatment plans and interventions for evidence-based psychotherapy. Guilford Press; 2012:xx, 490 p.

44. Leahy RL. *The worry cure : seven steps to stop worry from stopping you.* 1st ed. Harmony Books; 2005:x, 322 p.

45. Carnegie D. *How to win friends and influence people.* Simon and Schuster; 1936:x, 337, 5 p.

46. Schafer J, Karlins M. *The like switch : an ex-FBI agent's guide to influencing, attracting, and winning people over.* A Touchstone book. Simon & Schuster; 2015:xv, 270 pages.

47. Dhawan E. *Digital body language : how to build trust and connection, no matter the distance.* First edition. ed. St. Martin's Press; 2021:pages cm.

48. McCulloch G. *Because internet : understanding the new rules of language.* Riverhead Books; 2019:326 pages.

49. Organization. WH. Burn-out. Accessed 10/27/21, https://www.who.int/news/item/28-05-2019-burn-out-an-occupational-phenomenon-international-classification-of-diseases

50. Menon NK, Shanafelt TD, Sinsky CA, et al. Association of Physician Burnout With Suicidal Ideation and Medical Errors. *JAMA Netw Open.* Dec 1 2020;3(12):e2028780. doi:10.1001/jamanetworkopen.2020.28780

51. Morse G, Salyers MP, Rollins AL, Monroe-DeVita M, Pfahler C. Burnout in mental health services: a review of the problem and its remediation. *Adm Policy Ment Health.* Sep 2012;39(5):341-52. doi:10.1007/s10488-011-0352-1

52. Hall LH, Johnson J, Watt I, Tsipa A, O'Connor DB. Healthcare Staff Wellbeing, Burnout, and Patient Safety: A Systematic Review. *PloS one.* 2016;11(7):e0159015. doi:10.1371/journal.pone.0159015

53. Dyrbye LN, Massie FS, Jr., Eacker A, et al. Relationship between burnout and professional conduct and attitudes among US medical students. *JAMA.* Sep 15 2010;304(11):1173-80. doi:10.1001/jama.2010.1318

54. Stoewen DL. Dimensions of wellness: Change your habits, change your life. *Can Vet J.* Aug 2017;58(8):861-862.

55. Gazelle G, Liebschutz JM, Riess H. Physician burnout: coaching a way out. *J Gen Intern Med*. Apr 2015;30(4):508-13. doi:10.1007/s11606-014-3144-y

56. Huffington AS. *Thrive : the third metric to redefining success and creating a life of well-being, wisdom, and wonder*. First edition. ed. Harmony Books; 2014:342 pages.

57. Covey SR. *The seven habits of highly effective people : restoring the character ethic*. 1st Fireside ed. Fireside Book; 1990:358 p.

58. Straus SE, Chatur F, Taylor M. Issues in the mentor-mentee relationship in academic medicine: a qualitative study. *Acad Med*. Jan 2009;84(1):135-9. doi:10.1097/ACM.0b013e31819301ab

59. Murray B, Sikora A. Teaching the pursuit of sustainable excellence [published online ahead of print, 2022 Jun 7]. *Am J Health Syst Pharm*. 2022;zxac159. doi:10.1093/ajhp/zxac159.

A MENTOR'S BOOKSHELF

Organizational Psychology

Think Again by Adam Grant

Give & Take by Adam Grant

The Infinite Game by Simon Sinek

Peak by Robert Pool & Anders Ericsson

Grit by Angela Duckworth

To Sell is Human by Daniel Pink

Behavioral Economics

Thinking, Fast & Slow by Daniel Kahneman

Black Swan: The Impact of the Highly Improbable by Nassim Nicholas Taleb

Wellness

Thrive: The Third Metric to Redefining Success and Creating a Life of Well-Being, Wisdom, and Wonder by Ariana Huffington

Well Being: The Five Essential Elements by Tom Rath

The Dharma of the Princess Bride by Ethan Nichtern

The Upside of Stress by Kelly McGonigal

The Worry Cure: Seven Steps to Stop Worry from Stopping You by Robert L. Leahy

Living Beautifully: with Uncertainty and Change by Pema Chödrön

The Index Card: Why personal finance doesn't have to be complicated by Helaine Olen and Harold Pollack

Personal Management

Essentialism: The Disciplined Pursuit of Less by Greg McKeown

7 Habits of Highly Effective People by Stephen R. Covey

Eat that Frog! 21 Great Ways to Stop Procrastinating and Get More Done in Less Time by Brian Tracy

Deep Work by Cal Newport

Digital Minimalism by Cal Newport

Power of Habit by Charles Duhigg

Habit Stacking by S. J. Scott

Personality Inventories

Emotional Intelligence 2.0 by Travis Bradberry, Jean Greaves, and Patrick Lencioni

Type Talk: The 16 Personality Types That Determine How We Live, Love, and Work by Otto Kroeger and Janet M. Theusen

Strengths Finder 2.0 by Tom Rath, David de Vries, et al.

Introvert Power: Why Your Inner Life is Your Hidden Strength by Laurie Helgoe

The Secret Lives of Introverts: Inside our Hidden World by Jenn Granneman and Adrianne Lee

Quiet: The Power of Introverts in a World that Can't Stop Talking by Susan Cain

The Healthcare Experience

House of God by Samuel Shem

Wit: A Play by Margaret Edson

In Shock by Rana Awdish

Complications, Better, and Checklist Manifesto, all by Atul Gawande

When Breath Becomes Air by Paul Kalanithi

7 Signs of Life by Aoife Abbey

You Can Stop Humming Now by Daniela Lamas

My Stroke of Insight by Jill Bolte Taylor

Butterfly and The Diving Bell by Jean-Dominique Bauby and Jeremy Leggatt

The Man Who Mistook His Wife for a Hat by Oliver Sacks

Every Deep-Drawn Breath by Wes Ely

Emperor of all Maladies by Siddartha Mukherjee

The Gene by Siddartha Mukherjee

The Laws of Medicine by Siddartha Mukherjee

Team Building & Leadership

Dare to Lead by Brené Brown

Daring Greatly by Brené Brown

Lead Yourself First by Raymond Kethledge and Michael Erwin

Crucial Conversations: Tools for talking when the stakes are high by Kerry Patterson, Joseph Grenny, et al.

The Five Dysfunctions of a Team by J-B Lencioni

The Ideal Team Player: How to Recognize and Cultivate the Three Essential Virtues by J-B Lencioni

True North: Discover Your Authentic Leadership by Bill George and Peter Sims

The Making of a Manager by Julie Zhou

A Message to Garcia by Elbert Hubbard

Communication

Conversational Intelligence by Judith Glasir

How to Win Friends and Influence People by Dale Carnegie

The Like Switch: An Ex-FBI Agent's Guide to Influencing, Attracting, and Winning People Over by Jack Schafer

Digital Body Language by Erica Dhawan

It's not all about me: the top ten techniques for building quick rapport with anyone by Robin Dreeke

Education

Make It Stick by Peter C. Brown, Qarie Marshall, et al.

Mindset: The New Psychology of Success by Carol S. Dweck

Drive by Daniel Pink

Diversity, Equity, and Inclusion

Don't Label Me by Irshad Manji

Just Mercy by Bryan Stevenson

Bluest Eyes by Toni Morrison

Love Poems by Nikki Giovanni

Lord of the Butterflies by Andrea Gibson

Science

Lab Girl by Hope Jahren

Charlatan: America's Most Dangerous Huckster, The Man Who Pursued Him and the Age of FlimFlam by Pope Brock

Dr. Mutter's Marvels: A True Tale of Intrigue and Innovation at the Dawn of Modern Medicine by Cristin O'Keefe Aptowicz

End of Life

A Grief Observed by C.S. Lewis

Being Mortal by Atul Gawande

The Last Lecture by Randy Pausch

The Death of Ivan Ilyich by Leo Tolstoy

Mentorship

Power Mentoring by Ellen A. Ensher and Susan E. Murphy

10 Steps to Successful Mentoring by Wendy Axelrod

JOURNAL CLUB QUESTIONS FOR DISCUSSION

1. What role have mentors served in your career?

2. What role have mentees served in your career?

3. What is the best piece of feedback a mentor (or mentee) has ever given you?

4. What are the ideal traits of a mentor?

5. What are the ideal traits of a mentee?

6. How do structured mentoring or advising programs work to increase mentoring relationships?

7. What do you think are the biggest challenges mentors face?

8. What are the biggest challenges mentees face?

9. What level of professional responsibility do you feel towards mentorship?

10. Are mentorship activities part of the annual review process (and should it be included)?

11. As a mentor, it can be helpful to consider what your core principles and what concepts do you hope to imbue in your mentees. What your maxims? (see following page for some additional ideas)

MY 7 MENTORSHIP MAXIMS

1. **Define your purpose:** Identify your why. Write a personal mission or slogan. What wakes you up in the morning?

2. **Set your own bar for excellence:** Define success on a personal level. Seek challenge. Embrace a growth mindset and feedback. Realize that people involved in your healthcare training are trying to help you be the best version of you. Avoid the trap of coasting.

3. **Cultivate "no ego" and a servant mindset:** Healthcare is a career of serving others. You are a servant. Laugh at yourself. Making mistakes and asking for help are necessary. Everyone has something to teach you.

4. **Have mentors:** Build relationships. Be curious. Cultivate gratitude.

5. **Identify non-negotiables and sharpen the saw:** Feel secure in who you are but also keep in mind who you are yet to be. You are your own best employee: invest in your development and wellness. Forgive yourself. Be thoughtful of sustainable excellence.

6. **Metrics matter (but remember it's nature over number):** Your career is a journey, not a destination (as a mentor of mine said, "Your reward for all of this hard work is more hard work, but the work IS the reward"). Celebrate success. Assess ROI for how activities relate to goals. Keep your CV updated. Be deliberate with how you spend your time.

7. **Pay it forward:** The highest calling is helping those who cannot help themselves. Pay the gifts you have received forward. Find ways to lift others up. Kindle the fire of those you mentor. Be professionally generous (give more than you take). Know your boundaries but tend towards the gracious and graceful.

This book is written in Minion Pro, a serif typeface inspired by late Renaissance-era type. It was designed by Robert Slimbach and first released in 1990.

The gingko tree is the official tree of Athens, Georgia. Athens is named in honor of Athena, the goddess of wisdom and the heroine in one of the oldest stories of sharing wisdom and support to someone along their difficult journey.

Thank You

This book is possible only through the people who have never stopped believing in me: my family and friends, my preceptors and professors, and of course, my mentors and my mentees. Thank you, Mom and Dad. Thank you, Bobby. Thank you, Sarah. To anyone I've ever called my old friend, thank you for being you. Thank you, Susan, who opened my eyes to so much and who has been my timeless resource through every step. You all have provided endless love and support. You patch together my soul.

Isn't that a strange thing? That absolutely nothing changes except you see things differently and you're less fearful...and generally stronger as a result: Isn't that amazing that a completely invisible thing in your head can feel realer than anything? – **Jonathan Franzen**

*A final story. The water glasses were sweating rings on the polished pine table as we ate burgers and laughed. The topic was the latest dystopian teen movie and how they were pretty formulaic but still fun to watch. I joked that I was burned-out and going to quit my job to make it big writing one of those novels, "They're all the same. It'd be easy to do." Two laughed, but the third went stone still. His face looked physically pained. His concern at my glib proposal evident. "Not for your Heart Work," he finally said, the softness and intensity of the words struck me. Only when I promised I wouldn't do that did his tension ease. His belief in me that I had more in me than to do something because it was easy or to do anything that my full heart was not in meant more than words could say. I sat there, lost in thought. What was my Heart Work? It was a moment that can never be repaid. Ever since, when I have felt the urge to write, I place it in a folder titled Heart Work. I'd like to think this is a bit more of what you had in mind that day. It's what I've been trying to do ever since: **pay it forward**.*

Made in the USA
Coppell, TX
12 January 2023